Lippstadt Varieties

Performance · Quality · Resistance

DSV has an objective to produce high yielding oil seed rape varieties with stable broad spectrum disease resistance.

In our very extensive breeding programmes plant material is selected with equal emphasis on high seed yield and oil content combined with low erucic acid and glucosinolate content, and resistance to the most frequently occuring oilseed rape diseases.

Screening is carried out by artificially infecting plants with inoculum in both glasshouse and field trials. We also apply modern biotechnological selection procedures in the DSV laboratory for genetic disease control.

By concentrating the breeding on disease resistances, DSV is responding to todays economic and ecological demands in rape seed production.

Lippstadt oilseed rape varieties excel in their practical disease resistance characteristics and in addition show great response to fungicides when disease epidemics occur.

DSV have trial sites situated in various locations of the United Kingdom where their varieties are closely monitored for resistance to differing climatic and disease stresses. As a result of these rigourous testing procedures, DSV varieties offer the United Kingdom grower a wider choice of material specifically selected for local condition.

Lippstädter Sorten
Ertrag • Qualität • Resistenz

Deutsche Saatveredelung

4780 Lippstadt, Weissenburger Str. 5, Tel.: 0 29 41/1 70 61
Fax: 0 29 41/2 24 10, Telex: 084 401

DISEASES AND PESTS
OF RAPE

Volker H. Paul

C. J. Rawlinson

VERLAG TH. MANN · GELSENKIRCHEN-BUER

Adresses of the authors:
Prof. Dr. Volker H. Paul, Labor für Molekulare Phytopathologie
Universität – Gesamthochschule Paderborn, Warburger Straße 100, D-4790 Paderborn

Dr. C. J. Rawlinson
(formerly of Rothamsted Experimental Station), Harpenden, Herts AL5 5QN, England

Copyright 1992: Verlag Th. Mann, D-4650 Gelsenkirchen-Buer

Print: Buersche Druckerei Dr. Neufang KG, D-4650 Gelsenkirchen-Buer

ISBN 3-7862-0092-0

Introduction

The production of oilseed rape since the mid -1970s has increased more than any other crop in Europe. It has undergone two major changes, firstly the breeding and successful cultivation of low erucic acid cultivars then the production of those with low glucosinolate.

The extension of oilseed rape has been accompanied by an increase in the pests and pathogens specific to the crop. This book aims to meet increasing requests for easily understood information about the numerous agents causing disease and damage on oilseed rape.

The main subjects treated in this volume are the visual diagnosis of biotic and abiotic causes of damage and the biology of fungal diseases and of pests.

Knowledge of infection and infestation mechanisms and the economic importance of the various diseases and pests is an essential requirement for integrated crop protection with low environmental impact. The natural enemies of some pests are mentioned and threshold levels for sprays are quoted where their practical value is proven. Advice on control treatments is omitted since these are under continous change and review.

Literature of general interest is cited at the end of the volume. The papers cited in the text are not only to document some of the sources used in the compilation of the book, but also to give suggestions for further reading on specific topics. The book is mainly dedicated to consultants in crop husbandry and crop protection and to the growers of oilseed rape. In addition, it is a source of information on diseases and pests of oilseed rape for students of agricultural science.

The wide coverage of subjects has been possible only with the help and generous advice of numerous colleagues. Above all we wish to express our gratitude to Dr. Wilhelm Krüger (Braunschweig) for many important suggestions and critical advice and for revision of the manuscript. Parts of the book have been kindly scrutinized by docent Dr. H. Basedow (Gießen), Prof. H. Beringer (Hannover), Dr. R. Büchi (Zürich), Dr. D. Cooper (London), Dr. G. Jürgens (Limburgerhof), Prof. J. P. Tewari (Edmonton) and Dr. J. Müller (Münster).

We owe thanks to Dipl.-Ing. agr. G. Weiß (Bonn) and to the Headteacher of a secondary school Dipl.-Biol. H.-N. Gnacke (Solingen) for their professional support, to Mrs. Ch. Theilig (Essen) for her technical help and to Mr. A. Günzelmann (Soest) for the initial English translation.

Finally, we would like to express our thanks to the publishers Th. Mann Verlag for their patience and for their generosity in the presentation of the volume.

Paderborn, February 1992 and Harpenden, March 1992

Volker H. Paul and Chris J. Rawlinson

Summary

Growth Stages of Oilseed Rape
(Brassica napus) 12

PARASITIC DISEASES

Virus Diseases

Turnip Mosaic 16
Turnip Yellow Mosaic 16
Cauliflower Mosaic 16
Beet Western Yellows 17

Fungal Diseases

Clubroot
Plasmodiophora brassicae 18

Downy Mildew
Peronospora parasitica 22

Powdery Mildew
Erysiphe cruciferarum 26

Stem Canker
Phoma lingam
(Leptosphaeria maculans) 27

Stem Rot
Sclerotinia sclerotiorum 33

Dark Leaf and Pod Spot
Alternaria brassicae 38

Grey Mould
Botrytis cinerea
(Sclerotinia fuckeliana) 42

Typhula Root Rot
Typhula gyrans 44

Verticillium Wilt
Verticillium dahliae 46

Light Leaf Spot
Cylindrosporium concentricum
(Pyrenopeziza brassicae) 50

White Leaf Spot
*Pseudocercosporella capsellae
(Mycosphaerella capsellae)* 55

Ramularia Leaf Spot
Ramularia armoraciae 59

White Rust
Albugo candida 59

Ring Spot
Mycosphaerella brassicicola 60

Sore Shin & Damping off
*Rhizoctonia solani
(Thanatephorus cucumeris)* 62

PESTS

Slugs

Reticulated Field Slug
Deroceras reticulatum 66

Grey Field Slug
Deroceras agreste 67

Beetles and Weevils

Cabbage Stem Flea Beetle
Psylliodes chrysocephala 68

Turnip Gall Weevil
Ceutorhynchus pleurostigma 72

Rape Stem Weevil
Ceutorhynchus napi 74

Cabbage Stem Weevil
Ceutorhynchus quadridens 78

Rape Winter Stem Weevil
Ceutorhynchus picitarsis 81

Cabbage Seed Weevil
Ceutorhynchus assimilis 84

Pollen (Blossom) Beetle
Meligethes aeneus 87

Flies and Midges	Cabbage Root Fly *Delia radicum*	90
	Cabbage Leaf Miner *Phytomyza rufipes*	91
	Brassica Pod Midge *Dasineura brassicae*	92
Sawflies	Turnip Sawfly *Athalia rosae*	94
Aphids	Cabbage Aphid *Brevicoryne brassicae*	96
Nematodes	Brassica Cyst Nematode *Heterodera cruciferae*	99
	Root Lesion Nematode *Pratylenchus neglectus*	99
	Beet Cyst Nematode *Heterodera schachtii*	99
	Stem Eelworm *Ditylenchus dipsaci*	99
Birds	Woodpigeon *Columba palumbus*	100
	Sparrows and Finches *Passer spp., Carduelis spp.*	101
Mammals	Wild Rabbit *Oryctolagus cuniculus*	102
	Black Water Rat *Arvicola terrestris*	102
	Hare *Lepus europaeus*	102
	Common Vole *Microtus arvalis*	102

Benefical Insects

Honey Bee
Apis mellifera 103

Pest Detection and Targeted Control

Yellow Dish Trap 104

NONPARASITIC DISEASES

Frost Damage

Frost Damage 108
Late Frost Damage 110

Hail Injury

. . . . 112

Herbicide Damage

. . . . 114

Drought Damage

Bud Wilting 116
Growth Splits 116

Nitrogen Scorch

. . . . 117

Nutritional Disorders

Nitrogen Deficiency 118
Potassium Deficiency 118
Magnesium Deficiency 119
Calcium Deficiency 120
Copper Deficiency 120
Manganese Deficiency 121
Molybdenum Deficiency 121
Boron Deficiency 122
Phosphorus Deficiency 124
Sulphur Deficiency 125

Appendix

Glossary 128
General References 129
Index 130
Acknowledgement of Photographs 132

Growth Stages of Oilseed Rape (Brassica napus)

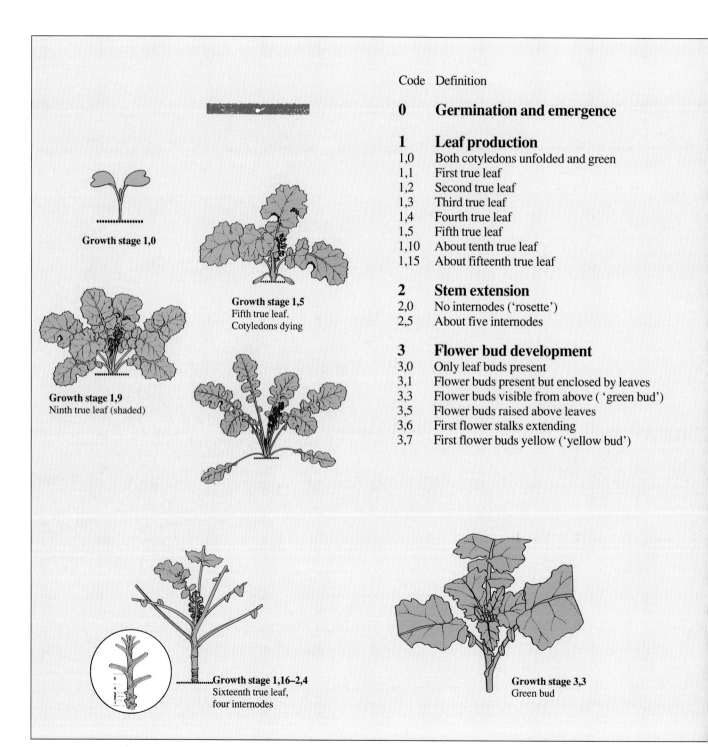

Code	Definition
0	**Germination and emergence**
1	**Leaf production**
1,0	Both cotyledons unfolded and green
1,1	First true leaf
1,2	Second true leaf
1,3	Third true leaf
1,4	Fourth true leaf
1,5	Fifth true leaf
1,10	About tenth true leaf
1,15	About fifteenth true leaf
2	**Stem extension**
2,0	No internodes ('rosette')
2,5	About five internodes
3	**Flower bud development**
3,0	Only leaf buds present
3,1	Flower buds present but enclosed by leaves
3,3	Flower buds visible from above ('green bud')
3,5	Flower buds raised above leaves
3,6	First flower stalks extending
3,7	First flower buds yellow ('yellow bud')

Growth stage 1,0

Growth stage 1,5
Fifth true leaf.
Cotyledons dying

Growth stage 1,9
Ninth true leaf (shaded)

Growth stage 1,16–2,4
Sixteenth true leaf,
four internodes

Growth stage 3,3
Green bud

4   Flowering

4,0	First flower opened
4,1	10% all buds opened
4,3	30% all buds opened
4,5	50% all buds opened

5   Pod development

5,3	30% potential pods
5,5	50% potential pods
5,7	70% potential pods
5,9	All potential pods

6   Seed development

6,1	Seed expanding
6,2	Most seeds translucent but full size
6,3	Most seeds green
6,4	Most seeds green-brown mottled
6,5	Most seeds brown
6,6	Most seeds dark brown
6,7	Most seeds black but soft
6,8	Most seeds black and hard
6,9	All seeds black and hard

7   Leaf senescence

8   Stem senescence

8,1	Most stem green
8,5	Half stem green
8,9	Little stem green

9   Pod senescence

9,1	Most pods green
9,5	Half pods green
9,9	Few pods green

Sylvester–Bradey, R. and Makepeace, R. J., 1984:
A code for stages of development in oilseed rape
(*Brassica napus L.*). Aspects of Applied Biology
6, 392–419.

Growth stage 4,0
First flower opened

Growth stage 4,1
10 % of all buds on
main stem flowering

Growth stage 4,7–5,2
70 % of all buds on main
stem flowering. 20 % of all
pods on main stem more
than 2 cm long

Growth stage 6,4–6,8
Seed development. Stages of ripening
of the seed when seed colour changes

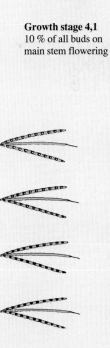

Parasitic Diseases

Virus Diseases

Virus diseases have been reported on oilseed rape but as yet have not been a serious problem for the crop. Frequently diagnosis is made difficult by mixed infections of more than one virus and sometimes symptoms caused by viruses resemble those caused by nutrient or mineral deficiencies.

Turnip Mosaic

Symptoms

The disease is caused by turnip mosaic virus or cabbage black ringspot virus.

The leaves of affected plants show an irregularly distributed mosaic which, on older leaves, may become necrotic accompanied by leaf distortion. First symptoms on leaves may be noticed as early as autumn, although generally the virus is more apparent in spring when affected plants are often stunted. In mixed infections with other viruses mosaic may be accompanied by leaf-crinkling. At the end of flowering, stems, pedicels and pods can show necrotic spots or streaks with raised black margins, later pods can be twisted and distorted.

Transmission and hosts

The disease is transmitted by many aphid species, notably the peach potato aphid *(Myzus persicae)* and the cabbage aphid *(Brevicoryne brassicae)*. All types of cultivated brassicas and many species of wild cruciferae are possible hosts of the virus.

Literature
Walsh, J A. & Tomlinson, J A., 1985: Viruses infecting winter oilseed rape *(Brassica napus* ssp. *oleifera)*. Annals of Applied Biology **107**, 485–495.

Turnip Yellow Mosaic

Symptoms

The disease is caused by turnip yellow mosaic virus.

The leaves of infected plants first show vein clearing and chlorotic patches then are chequered with vivid yellow patches which later may turn fawn in colour and coalesce. Severe deformations such as leaf-crinkling are absent. (Vein clearing by another virus, broccoli necrotic yellows, has also been recorded in rape). This disease has not been reported in oilseed rape in Britain.

Transmission and hosts

The virus is transmitted by various biting insects such as stem weevils and cabbage stem flea beetles. Besides oilseed rape all types of cabbage, turnip rape and numerous wild cruciferae are attacked.

Cauliflower Mosaic

Symptoms

The disease is caused by cauliflower mosaic virus. The veins of the youngest and, later, also of the older leaves are first cleared and then become yellowish. Other leaf symptoms resemble those of turnip mosaic, with mosaics, dark green vein banding and necrosis, sometimes with distorted leaves and short petioles. When severely attacked the plants are stunted.

Transmission and hosts

Cauliflower mosaic virus is transmitted by many aphid species, commonly by the mealy cabbage aphid *(Brevicoryne brassicae)* and the peach potato aphid *(Myzus persicae)*. The host range of the virus also includes cabbage, turnip rape, stubble turnips and many other species of cruciferae.

Beet Western Yellows

Symptoms

Beet western yellows virus was detected in winter oilseed rape in England in 1975 and is now widespread there. It can cause an intense interveinal yellowing of the lower and middle leaves ❶ ❷ in some cultivars, often with purpling, but others may be symptomless.

Transmission and Hosts

The virus is most commonly transmitted by the peach potato aphid *(Myzus persicae)*. The possibility of infrequent transmission from infected sugar beet crops to oilseed rape and viceversa has been demonstrated.

Literature

Hill, S. A., Lane, A. and Hardwick, N. V., 1991: The incidence and importance of beet western yellows virus in oilseed rape. IOBC/WPRS Bulletin XIV (6), 36-45.
Smith, H. G. & Hinckes, J. A., 1985: Studies on beet western yellows virus in oilseed rape *(Brassica napus* ssp. *oleifera)* and sugar beet *(Beta vulgaris)*. Annals of Applied Biology, **107**, 473-484.

Fungal Diseases

Clubroot *Plasmodiophora brassicae* Wor.

Causal Organism and Symptoms

Clubroot disease is caused by the soilborne fungus Plasmodiophora brassicae Wor.

Affected plants are stunted and their older leaves turn prematurely yellowish or red in colour ❶, ❷. If autumn is dry and warm plants may wilt and patches of well distinguished stunted plants can be seen in the field ❶, ❹.

Irregular red-brown swellings with an uneven surface ❸ develop on main and lateral roots. These swellings are white and solid inside and therefore easy to distinguish from those caused by the cabbage gall weevil *(Ceutorhynchus pleurostigma)* which are hollow inside and of regular shape. Advanced stages of clubroot attack are characterized by bulbous gall ❺, ❻ which are greyish inside and begin to decay at the end of the growing period.

Biology

The flagellate spores (zoospores) (1) of the fungus are motile in soil water. In contact with the host plant (2) they penetrate into the root-hairs (3) and produce a multinucleate aggregate (plasmodium) (4) which later is transformed in a sporangium and releases secondary zoospores (5). The latter may pass through the wall of the root-hair into the soil and cause secondary infections of other root-hairs, or they may migrate to the base of the infected root-hair and penetrate further into root tissues. The initially binucleate plasmodium (6) in the cortical tissues undergoes several divisions to produce a multinucleate plasmodium (7.1). Infected cells become hypertrophied while division of the neighbouring cells is stimulated thus forming the macroscopic galls on the main and lateral roots (7.2). As soon as the galls decay resting spores are liberated (8, 9) which germinate in contact with soil water and transmit the infection to other roots.

The resting spores are very durable and remain viable for ten to twenty years.

Temperatures between 20 and 30 °C, waterlogged soils, insufficient aeration and calcium-deficiency are favourable for spore germination and infection.

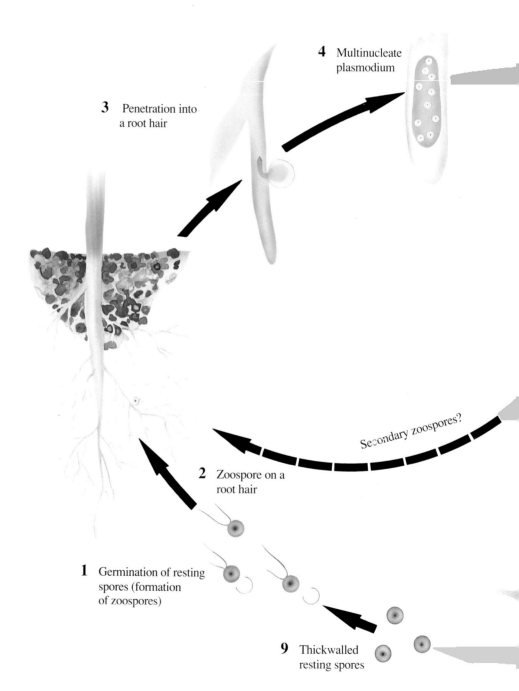

4 Multinucleate plasmodium

3 Penetration into a root hair

Secondary zoospores?

2 Zoospore on a root hair

1 Germination of resting spores (formation of zoospores)

9 Thickwalled resting spores

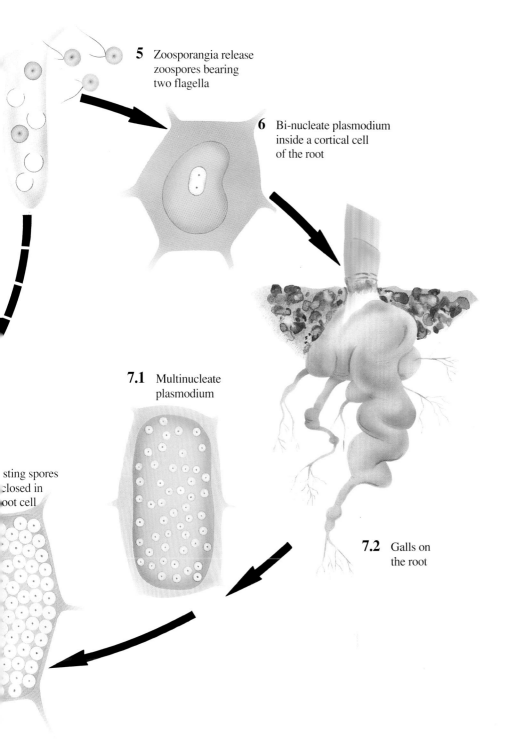

5 Zoosporangia release zoospores bearing two flagella

6 Bi-nucleate plasmodium inside a cortical cell of the root

7.1 Multinucleate plasmodium

7.2 Galls on the root

sting spores
closed in
oot cell

Host Range

P. brassicae can infect all cultivated and wild cruciferae. Besides oilseed rape, swede, turnip rape, and mustard are attacked. All types of vegetable and forage brassicas are susceptible, although radish is less severely affected. Possible hosts among the wild cruciferae are field pennycress, charlock, wild radish and shepherd's purse.

Occurrence and Importance

Clubroot disease is favoured by crop rotations which include frequent oilseed rape. The disease is common on acid, poorly drained soils and in regions where other brassicas are grown. On rape the disease is of local importance with consistent damage occuring on certain sites only.

Literature
Clarkson, J. D. S. & Brockenshire. T., 1984: Incidence of clubroot in oilseed rape crops in England, Wales and Scotland. British Crop Protection Conference on Pests and Diseases, **2**, 723—728.

Downy Mildew *Peronospora parasitica* (Pers.) Fr.

Causal Organism and Symptoms

Downy Mildew is caused by the fungus *Peronospora parasitica* (Pers.) Fr.

The upper surfaces of affected young ❶❷ and older leaves, ❸, ❹, ❺, ❼, ❾, have ill-defined, irregular, pale yellow areas, sometimes with necrosis, which are covered on the lower surface by white-grey mycelium ❻, ❽. The cotyledons and older leaves may be killed prematurely by severe attacks when single lesions coalesce to form large blotches.

Attacked pods may be covered with angular fawn-brown lesions or, under conditions of high humidity, a sparse greyish-white sporulating mycelium can develop which might be confused with grey mould *(Botrytis cinerea)*. Severe attacks may lead to a slight bronzing of the whole pod and to premature ripening.

Biology

The fungus survives as oospores (1.1) sexually produced by the union of oogonium and antheridium (6) in decaying crop debris, as conidia on the lower surfaces of the oldest leaves of rape volunteers (1.2) or as latent, systemic mycelium on other species of cruciferae. Infections (2, 3, 4, 5) are favoured by temperatures between 10 and 15 °C and by high atmospheric humidity following rain, mist or heavy dew. The

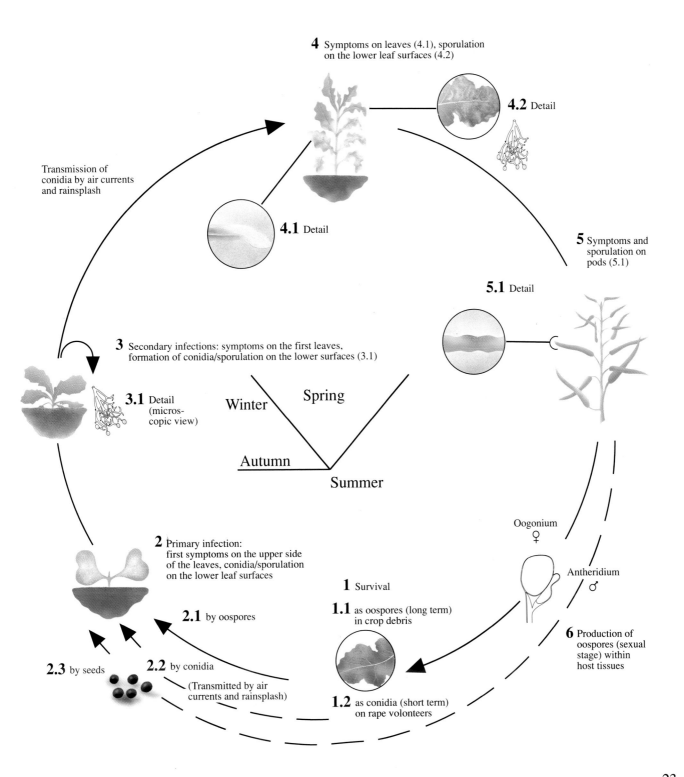

4 Symptoms on leaves (4.1), sporulation on the lower leaf surfaces (4.2)

4.2 Detail

4.1 Detail

Transmission of conidia by air currents and rainsplash

5 Symptoms and sporulation on pods (5.1)

5.1 Detail

3 Secondary infections: symptoms on the first leaves, formation of conidia/sporulation on the lower surfaces (3.1)

3.1 Detail (micro-scopic view)

Winter

Spring

Autumn

Summer

Oogonium ♀

Antheridium ♂

2 Primary infection: first symptoms on the upper side of the leaves, conidia/sporulation on the lower leaf surfaces

1 Survival

1.1 as oospores (long term) in crop debris

2.1 by oospores

6 Production of oospores (sexual stage) within host tissues

2.3 by seeds

2.2 by conidia

(Transmitted by air currents and rainsplash)

1.2 as conidia (short term) on rape volonteers

spores produce germ-tubes which penetrate anticlinal cell walls, often on the lower surfaces of leaves and then spread in the leaf tissues. Transmission by infected seed (2.3) is possible but there are no reports about its importance for the spread of the disease. The fungus is spread by terminal conidia borne on dichotomously branched conidiophores which emerge through the stomatal openings on the lower leaf surface. Conidia are dispersed aerially when conidiophores twist during changes in humidity, or by rain splash.

Host Range

P. parasitica occurs on numerous species of cultivated and wild cruciferae such as shepherd's purse and field penny cress.

Occurrence and Importance

In Sweden and Poland downy mildew is regarded as one of the most injurious diseases of oilseed rape. In Germany and Britain severe attacks have been observed in certain years in autumn on seedlings and younger plants. Infection may continu through spring until flowerin and pod formation, especially the season is humid and cool an if autumn infections were wel established. The effect of au tumn or spring infections o yield is not yet well known; loss es of 10 to 15% have been re corded from Poland.

Literature

Hardwick, N. V., Culshaw. F. A., Davies, M. L., Gladders, P., Hawkins, J. H. and Lawson, D. D., 1989: Incidence and severity of fungal diseases of winter oilseed rape in England and Wales, 1986–1988. Aspects of Applied Biology, **23**, 383–392.

Lucas, J. A. ,1988: *Peronospora parasitica, (Pers.) Fr.* In „European Handbook of Plant Diseases" Eds. I. M. Smith et al. Blackwell Scientific Publications, Oxford pp. 218-220.

Nashaat, N. I. and Rawlinson, C. J., 1991: Resistance to downy mildew in *Brassica napus* ssp. *oleifera*. IOBC/WPRS Bulletin XIV (6), 166–173.

Paul, V. H., Burhenne S. and Günzelmann, A., 1991: Preliminary results of research on *Peronospora parasitica* (Pers.) Fr. in winter oilseed rape with special regard to the suceptibility of double low cultivars. International Organisation for Biological an Integrated Control of Noxious Animals and Plants (WPRS), Bulletin XIV, (6), 174–180.

Sadowski, Cz., 1989: An investigation on the occurrence and control of downy mildew on winter rapeseed. 7th Intern. Rapeseed Congress 1987 Poznan. Proceedings 5, 1097–1103.

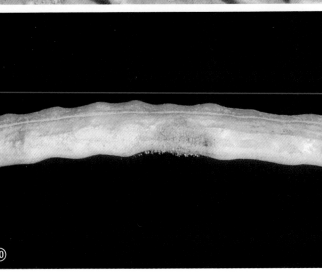

Powdery Mildew *Erysiphe cruciferarum* Opiz ex Junell

Causal Organism and Symptoms

Powdery mildew is caused by the airborne fungus *Erysiphe cruciferarum* Opiz ex Junell.

Thin, diffuse powdery mycelium, initially white and later darkening to light-brown, can occur on leaves, petioles, stems or pods ❶, ❷, ❸, ❹.

Both upper and lower surfaces of leaves may be covered with areas of white mycelium measuring 1 to 2 cm im diameter, but attacks on the upper surface are more common ❶. In severe attacks the infected areas coalesce so that the leaves become mealy, dry and are killed prematurely.

Biology

Short chains of barrel-shaped unicellular conidia are produced on short conidiophores borne on the white mycelium. The conidia are aerially dispersed. Very small globose structures *(cleistothecia)*, the resting form of the fungus, are rarely produced at the end of the growing season under dry conditions. They contain the sexual spores (ascospores) of the fungus.

Development of the disease is favoured by temperatures ranging from 17 to 20 °C with periods of high humidity.

Host Range

Besides oilseed rape there are many other species of wild and cultivated cruciferae which are possible hosts of powdery mildew.

Occurrence and Importance

In autumn, powdery mildew is occasionally observed on oilseed rape if sunny, warm days with heavy dew formation a night persist for several weeks In a very dry, hot summer th sporulating mycelium can cov er large areas of the surface stems and pods. However, n economically important yiel losses have been recorded i Germany, France or Britain.

Stem Canker *Phoma lingam* (Tode ex Schw.) Desm. – *Leptosphaeria maculans*

Causal Organism and Symptoms

Stem canker or blackleg disease of oilseed rape is caused by the fungus Phoma lingam (Tode ex Schw.). Desm. and its sexual stage Leptosphaeria maculans (Desm.) Ces & de Not.

The first symptoms appear early in autumn as fawn spots ❶, ❷, on the leaves, often surrounded by yellowed tissue, sometimes bearing at their center numerous, tiny, dark-coloured, globose, fruiting bodies of the asexual stage (pycnidia) ❹. Frequently, the leaf surface is ruptured at the center of the spots ❷, ❹. Severely attacked leaves die prematurely before winter.

Sometimes in autumn the roots and root collar bear small black lesions ('blackleg'). In spring, lesions on the stembase enlarge and the affected part undergoes a dry rot and can girdle the stem. Later, this damage may cause lodging and premature ripening and even death of the whole plant ❸.

If winter is very cold, severe autumn attacks tend to be attenuated, the attacked leaves being killed by frost. Nevertheless the fruiting bodies (pycnidia) on the decaying leaves may remain viable.

In spring the infected stem tissues take on dark-brown colouration, become fissured and undergo dry rot ❺. Frequently the plants are severed from the root ❻, ❿, ⓬. Another symptom is dry rot of the root collar ⓫. Affected tissues peel off and the root collar is girdled with deep scars. The disease then spreads to the stem-base which becomes greyish-brown and dies. Attacks on higher parts of the stem are characterised by fawn to white discolourations with a dark brown margin.

Early attacks usually cause loss of the green stem colour, premature ripening and, sometimes, lodging.

Late attacks cause only fawn-coloured and slightly sunken lesions with a darker margin while the upper parts of the plants remain green ❼, ❽, ❾.

Similar lesions may occur on the pods ⓮.

On attacked tissues the black, globose fruiting bodies of the fungus (pycnidia) ⓭, are visible to the naked eye ❹, ❾. The fruiting bodies may be immersed in the host-tissues of leaves, stems and pods or superficial, the fungus having destroyed the surrounding tissues.

Biology

The life-cycle comprises a sexual stage *(Leptosphaeria maculans)* producing ascospores and an asexual stage *(Phoma lingam)* which produces pycnospores. Both spore types can initiate epidemics causing severe yield losses.

The fungus produces fruiting bodies (pseudothecia) ⓭ of the sexual stage, containing numerous multiseptate spores (ascospores) (8.2, 1.1), on infected plant debris mainly in September during rainy weather with temperatures up to 15 °C. The ascospores are liberated in autumn during warm and humid weather and remain viable for about six weeks. They infect young plants and produce lesions on the leaves and, sometimes, on the root collar (2). Asexual reproduction by unicellular pycnospores formed in pycnidia (3, 4) also occurs in autumn.

In northern and central Germany, where early and deep ploughing are common practice, the principal source of autumn infections is pycnospores (8.1, 1.2). In contrast, in France, Great Britain and Bavaria, where minimum cultivation or even direct drilling techniques are used, the main source is ascospores. During combine har-

vesting and after until cultivation, the pycnospores are transported by air to nearby fields. The spores which have landed on the soil may then infect the leaves or root collars of emerging seedlings (2).

The plants are invaded through the stomatal openings and through wounds. From infected leaves the fungus grows into the petioles and from there into the stem base and the root collar causing the symptoms described above.

Seedborne transmission by spores adhering to the seeds during combine harvesting is possible. Another, but less important, source of infection is contamination of seeds produced inside affected pods (7.1, 1.3).

In the field the disease is spread by wind and rain dispersing pycnospores (3–7). If temperatures in autumn are sufficiently high pycnidia may be produced before winter. The spores; when within both types of fruiting bodies, pseudothecia and pycnidia, remain viable for two to four years.

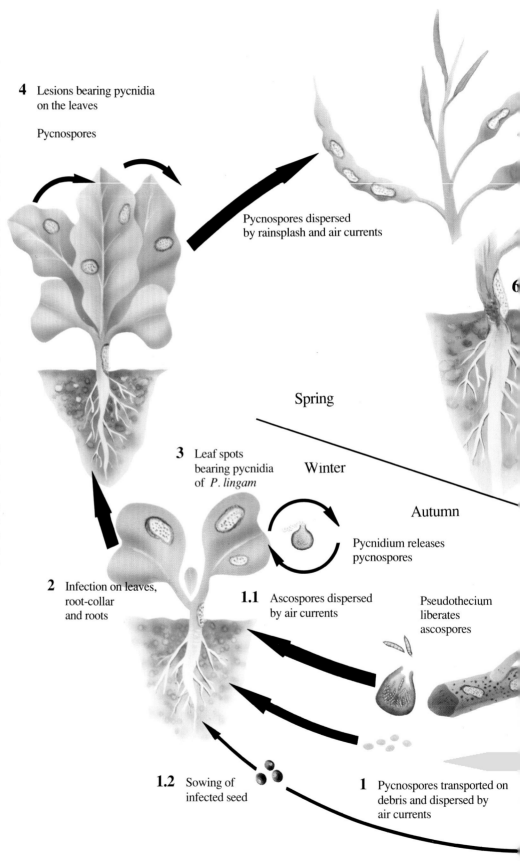

4 Lesions bearing pycnidia on the leaves

Pycnospores

Pycnospores dispersed by rainsplash and air currents

Spring

3 Leaf spots bearing pycnidia of *P. lingam*

Winter

Autumn

Pycnidium releases pycnospores

2 Infection on leaves, root-collar and roots

1.1 Ascospores dispersed by air currents

Pseudothecium liberates ascospores

1.2 Sowing of infected seed

1 Pycnospores transported on debris and dispersed by air currents

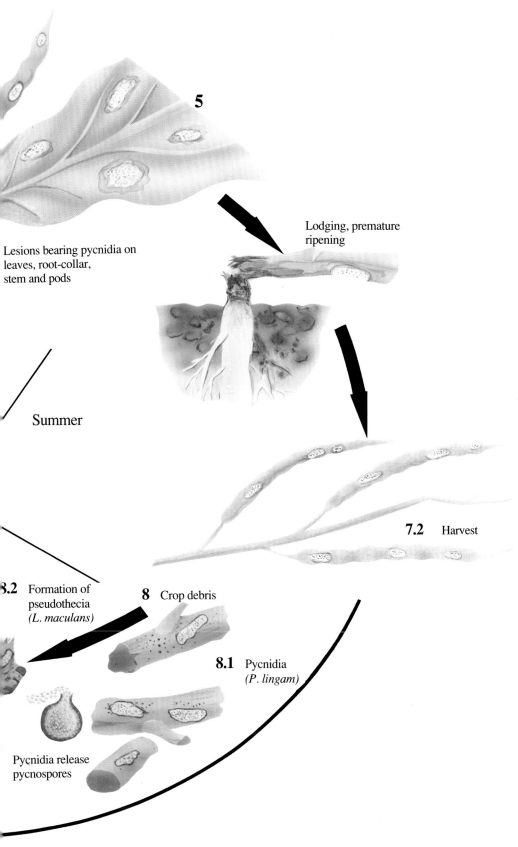

5

Lesions bearing pycnidia on
leaves, root-collar,
stem and pods

Lodging, premature
ripening

Summer

7.2 Harvest

8.2 Formation of
pseudothecia
(L. maculans)

8 Crop debris

8.1 Pycnidia
(P. lingam)

Pycnidia release
pycnospores

Host Range

The fungus has many poss-
ible hosts in the cruciferae.
Among the crops attacked are
vegetable brassicas, radish and
white mustard. Many other wild
cruciferae such as shepherd's
purse are possible hosts.

Occurrence and Importance

Stem canker is widespread
where oilseed rape is cultivated
and is one of the most important
diseases of the crop. Incidence
and damage vary with the season and cultivar. Severe autumn
attacks may increase plant mor-
tality overwinter and cause low
population densities. Harvesting may be made difficult by infected lodged plants.

Literature
Alabouvette, C. et Brunin, B. 1970: Recherches sur la maladie du colza due à
Leptosphaeria maculans (Desm.) Ces. et
de Not. I. – Rôle des restes de culture dans
la conservation et la dissemination du parasite. Ann. Phytopathol., **2** , 463–475.
Alabouvette, C., Brunin, B., et Louvet, J.,
1974: Recherches sur la maladie du colza
due à *Leptosphaeria maculans* (Desm.)
Ces. et de Not. IV. – Pouvoir infectieux
des pycniospores et sensibilité variétale.
Ann. Phytopathol., **6**, (3)
265-275.
Brunin, B. et Lacoste, L., 1970: Recherches sur la maladie du colza due à *Lepto-
sphaerta maculans* (Desm.) Ces. et Nol.
II.– Pouvoir pathogène des ascospores.
Ann. Phytopathol., **2** (3), 477–488.
Daebeler, F. und Pluschkell, H.-J. 1975:
Zum Auftreten von *Phoma lingam* (Tode
ex Fr.) Desm. an Winterraps in der DDR.
Nachr.Bl. Pflschutz. DDR **29** (5), 115–
116.

Daebeler, F., Amelung, D. und Engel, K. H., 1985: Zur Verwechslungsmöglichkeit der durch *Phoma lingam* (Tode ex Fr.) Desm. verursachten Wurzelhalsfäule mit *Rhizoctonia solani K.* und *Verticillium dahliae* Kleb.: Nachr. BL. Pflschutzd. DDR **39** (8), 180–181

Gabrielson, R. L., 1983: Blackleg disease of Crucifers caused by *Leptosphaeria maculans (Phoma lingam)* and its control. Seed Sci. of Technol., **11**, 749–780.

Krüger, W., 1979: Verbreitung der Wurzelhals- und Stengelfäule (verursacht durch *Phoma lingam)* bei Raps in der Bundesrepublik Deutschland, Nachr.BI. Dtschl. Pflschutzd. Braunschweig **31** (10), 145–148

Hammond, K. E., Lewis, B . G. & Musa, T. M. 1985: A systemic pathway in the infection of oilseed rape plants by *Leptosphaeria maculans*. Plant Pathology, **34**, 557-565.

Krüger, W., 1989: Über das Auftreten von Wurzel-, Wurzelhals- und Stengelfäule des Rapses sowie deren Erreger (1985–1987). Nachrichtenbl. Deutsch. Pflanzenschutzd, **41** (7) 97–103.

Krüger, W. und Wittern, I., 1985: Epidemiologische Untersuchungen bei der Wurzelhals- und Stengelfäule des Rapses, verursacht durch *Phoma lingam.* Phytopath. Z., **113**, 125–140.

Mc Gee, D. C., and Petrie, G. A., 1978: Variability of *Leptosphaeria maculans* in relation to blackly of oilseed rape. Phytopathology **68**, 625–630.

Paul, V. H., 1987: Investigation of the Infection of Winter Oilseed Rape by *Phoma lingam.* Integr. Control Oils. Rape. IOBC/WPRS Bulletin X(4), 38–41.

Paul, V. H., Gerdiken, K. J. and Günzmann, A., 1991: Resistance of Doub low Winter Rape Cultivars to Stem Ca ker and their Yield Response to Fungici Treatment. IOBC/WPRS Bulletin X (6), 67–73.

Stem Rot *Sclerotinia sclerotiorum* (Lib.) de Bary

Causal Organism and Symptoms

Stem rot, also called sclerotinia stem rot, to distinguish it from grey mould stem rot *(B. cinerea)*, is caused by the fungus *Sclerotinia sclerotiorum* (Lib.) de Bary.

Usually the first symptoms are seen after flowering. The lesions appear on the main stem and lateral branches as bleached or whitish areas with the margin tending to yellow and a more grey center ❹, ❺, ❻, ❼, ❽. The infection usually starts from a leaf insertion point and then spreads up and down the stem. Pods and stem portions situated above the lesions ripen prematurely or die ❶, ❷, ❸, ⓫. The prematurely ripened stems, named 'whiteheads', are easily distinguished in a normal, healthy crop. The pith and superficial tissues of the affected stem parts are destroyed; the stem is empty inside or filled with a fluffy whitish mycelium and with irregular shaped, initially greyish and then black resting forms of the fungus (sclerotia) ⓬, ⓭.

①

When pods are attacked they become yellowish and dry out. At harvest small black sclerotia (microsclerotia) may be found among the seeds.

Attacks on emerging seedlings or at the beginning of the growing season in spring have been reported from milder climates (e.g. valley of the Rhine, central France, south and east England). Leaves, petioles and shoot tips become light brown, undergo a soft rotting and may be killed. ln conditions of high humidity an external mycelium is formed and even sclerotia may be found on the surface of attacked parts ❾, ❿ .

Biology

The 3 to 15 mm long sclerotia formed inside and, with high humidity, also outside the stem may be liberated at harvest and fall on the soil ⑭, ⑮ or they may remain attached to the stem de-

bris and be ploughed under (1 A low percentage of sclerotia, i size and shape similar to th seeds of rape, is likely to be ha vested and sown the next yea The sclerotia remain viable fc 7–10 years (2) and will germ nate if they are buried in the up per layer (5 cm) of soil (2.1 They produce small, saucer shaped fruiting bodies (apothe

a) (2.2) which emerge above il level **⑯**, **⑰**. These sexual uiting bodies are orange to ght-brown and contain sac-ke cells (asci) enclosing spores scospores). These are actively berated and spread by air cur-nts (2.3). When in contact with aves or stems of the host (3.1) d under favourable atmos-heric conditions, the as-

cospores germinate and infect. Usually infection is facilitated by fallen petals, which serve as an initial source of nutrients for the arriving spores, collected in the axils of the upper leaves (4, 5).

Another possible method of infection of minor importance is by direct attack of roots and low-er stem parts by mycelium (3.2)

produced from germinating sclerotia in the upper soil layers (2.4).

High temperatures and hu-midity early in spring stimulate germination of sclerotia which may produce apothecia at the end of April or early May. Low soil moisture inhibits germina-tion completely. If eg. the soil dries out after the sclerotia ger-

minate, then the apothecia shrink and release only a few or no ascospores. Persistent rain-fall may wash the spores directly from the fruiting bodies into the soil and prevent infection. High temperatures and changeable humidity are the most favoura-ble conditions for spread of the disease.

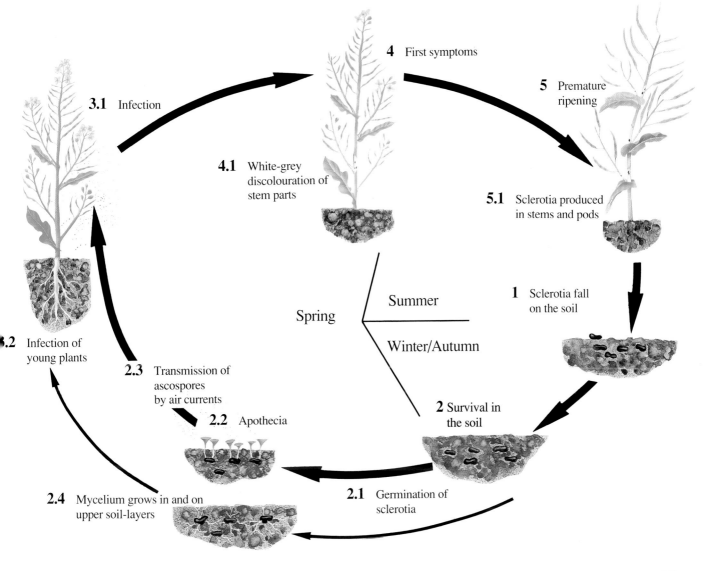

4 First symptoms

5 Premature ripening

3.1 Infection

4.1 White-grey discolouration of stem parts

5.1 Sclerotia produced in stems and pods

3.2 Infection of young plants

1 Sclerotia fall on the soil

Summer

Spring

Winter/Autumn

2.3 Transmission of ascospores by air currents

2 Survival in the soil

2.2 Apothecia

2.4 Mycelium grows in and on upper soil-layers

2.1 Germination of sclerotia

Infected plant parts do not produce spores, so the only method of transmission from lesions is by direct contact between plants. This can contribute to the disease forming patches in the field **❶**.

Host Range

S. sclerotiorum attacks a very wide range of wild and cultivated members of many families of dicotyledons: attacked crops are found among the Cruciferae, Leguminosae, Solanaceae, Chenopodiaceae, Umbelliferae and Compositae. Wild species which are hosts include mayweed, deadnettle, cleavers, chickweed, fat hen and field pansy.

Occurrence and Importance

Stem rot is common where oilseed rape is cultivated. Severe yield losses resulting from reduced seed weight and pod shattering occur in coastal regions and in humid, protected sites. The incidence varies between sites, dependent on previous cropping and seasonal conditions – especially favourable weather in spring.

Literature

...hlers, D., 1986: Untersuchungen über ...en Erreger der Weißstengeligkeit *Sclerotinia sclerotiorum* (Lib.) de Bary an ...interraps – Sortenresistenz – Epidemiologie – Krankheitsverlauf – Prognose. ...issertation, Bonn.

...run, H., Bautrais, P., Renard, M. & Tri-odet, M., 1983: Importance de ...humidité relative de l'air et de la temperature sur la contamination du colza par ...clerotinia sclerotiorum. 6 ème Congrès ...nternational sur le Colza, Paris, 897-902

Jellis, G. J., Davies, J. M. L. & Scott, E. S., 1984: Sclerotinia on oilseed rape: implications for crop rotation. Proceedings 1984 British Crop Protection Conference-Pests and Diseases, 2, 709–715.

Krüger, W., 1975a: Über die Wirkung der Witterung auf den Befall des Rapses durch *Sclerotinia sclerotiorum* (Lib.) de Bary. Nachrichtenbl. Dtsch. Pflanzenschutzd. **27**, 1–6.

Krüger, W., 1975b: Die Beeinflussung der Apothezien- und Ascosporenentwicklung des Rapskrebserregers *Sclerotinia sclerotiorum* (Lib.) de Bary durch Umweltfaktoren.Z.Pfl.Krank. Pfl.Schutz **82**, 101–108.

Krüger, W., 1975c: Über die Bildung von Sclerotien des Rapskrebserregers *Sclerotinia sclerotiorum*. Mitt. BBA **163**, 32-40.

Krüger, W., 1976: Untersuchungen zur Beeinflussung der Apothezienentwicklung von *Sclerotinia sclerotiorum* (Lib.) de Bary. Nachrichtenbl. Dtsch. Pflanzenschutzd. **28**, 129–135.

Lamarque, C., 1983: Conditions climatiques qui favorisent le processus naturel de contamination du colza par le *Sclerotinia sclerotiorum*. 6 ème Congrès International sur le Colza, Paris, 903–908.

Penaud, A., 1984: Les pétales et la contamination du colza par *Sclerotinia sclerotiorum*. Informations techniques. CETIOM no. 89. 20–28.

Dark Leaf and Pod Spot *Alternaria brassicae* (Berk.) Sacc.

Causal Organism and Symptoms

Dark leaf and pod spot is principally caused by two species of fungi from the Alternaria group, i.e. *Alternaria brassicae* (Berk.) Sacc. and *A. brassicicola* (Schw.) Wiltsh. *A. alternata,* and *A. raphani,* may also be involved.

In autumn, sometimes elongated, brown discolourations are seen on superficial tissues of hypocotyls and roots, which later undergo soft rot. In consequence, the root collar is girdled and seedlings lodge or damp-off.

More typically, cotyledons and foliage leaves become infected in autumn by *A. brassicae.* They are covered with char-acteristic brown spots of 0.5 to mm in diameter. Later the tru leaves bear small, black, circu lar, necrotic lesions with a ye. low margin ❷, ❹. Older leave have 2 to 15 mm large spots wit a well defined margin and alter nating dark and light brow

cones **1**, **2**, hence the Latin name of the fungus. Another type of foliage symptom occurs as 0.1 to 1 mm large, dark brown spots with a yellow margin. Severely attacked leaves undergo a yellowish-brown discolouration **3** and fall off.

The main stem and lateral branches can carry elongated, 1 to 5 mm long, black or light grey coloured flecks with a well defined margin **5**, **6**. Similar symptoms can occur on upper parts of racemes, and pedicels.

Affected pods are covered with black, usually circular areas of 0.5 to 3 mm in diameter **7**, **8**, **9**, **10**, **11**. Sometimes the spots are a light-grey colour with a black margin.

In humid conditions all attacked parts may be covered with a dark, velvety mycelium and spores.

⑤

⑥

⑦

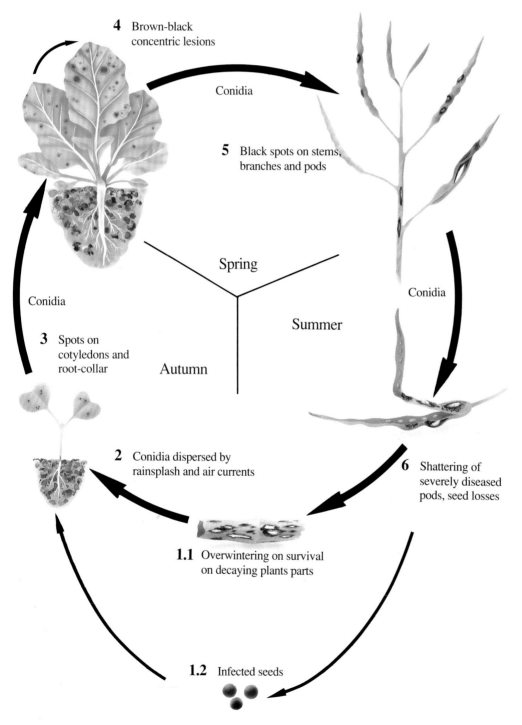

4 Brown-black concentric lesions

Conidia

5 Black spots on stems, branches and pods

Spring

Conidia

Conidia

Summer

3 Spots on cotyledons and root-collar

Autumn

2 Conidia dispersed by rainsplash and air currents

6 Shattering of severely diseased pods, seed losses

1.1 Overwintering on survival on decaying plants parts

1.2 Infected seeds

Biology

A. *brassicae* survives on infected plant debris and seed (1.1, 1.2). Primary attacks (3) spread usually from conidia produced on decaying stubbles and from infected seed (1.2). The life cycle continues during the growth period on leaves, stem and pods causing the symptom mentioned above (4, 5, 6).

The disease is favoured by warm (17 to 25 °C) and humid weather during flowering and maturation. Optimal conditions for spore germination are given by temperatures between 22 and 25 °C and by the presence of free water on the plant . Under these conditions infection is completed within four to six hours after spore deposition. The plant is invaded through the stomatal openings or directly through the cuticle. A. *brassicae* produces single or short chain of dark-brown, club-shaped conidia with muriforrn septation and a filiform beak.

The conidia are spread locally by rain splash and over considerable distances by wind.

Host Range

Many cultivated and wild cruciferae are hosts of A. *brassicae* and A. *brassicicola*. Most vegetable and forage brassicas and mustard are susceptible.

Occurrence and Importance

Dark leaf and pod spot is widespread in areas of oilseed rape cultivation. The incidence of the disease increases in protected sites with high atmospheric humidity. Significant yield losses can occur if during od formation periods of warm, umid weather are succeeded y dry, warm periods. The importance of other species of Alternaria, which cause identical or very similar symptoms, is not et clear. In France, south Germany, Poland, Britain and Canada dark leaf and pod spot is regarded as one of the major fungal diseases of oilseed rape.

Literature

Daebeler, F. and Amelung, D., 1988: Auftreten und Bedeutung der *Alternaria*-Rapsschwärze im Winterraps. Nachrichtenbl. Pfl. Schutzd. d.e. DDR **42** 196–199.

Domsch, K. H., 1957: Die Raps- und Kohlschotenschwärze. Z. Pflanzenkr. Pflanzenschutz **64**, 65–79.

Evans, E. J., Davies, H. M. L., Gladders, P., Hardwick, N. V., Hawkins, J. H., Jones, D. R. and Simkin, M. B., 1983: The occurrence and control of diseases of winter oilseed rape in England. Proceedings 6th International Rapeseed Conference **2**, 1032–1037.

Humpherson-Jones, F. M., 1983: The occurrence of *Alternaria brassicicola, Alternaria brassicae and Leptosphaeria maculans* in brassica seed crops in southeast England between 1976 and 1980. Plant Pathology. **32**, 33–39.

Joly, P., 1964: Le genre *Alternaria* Recherches physiologiques, biologiques et systématiques. – Editions P. Chevalier, Paris.

Louvette, J. et Bilotte, J. M., 1964: Influence des facteurs climatiques sur les infections du colza par l'*Alternaria brassicae* et conséquences pour la lutte. Annales Epiphyties **15**, 229–243.

Tewari, J.P., 1986: Subcuticular growth of *Alternaria brassicae* in rapeseed. Canadian Journal of Botany **64**, 1227–1231.

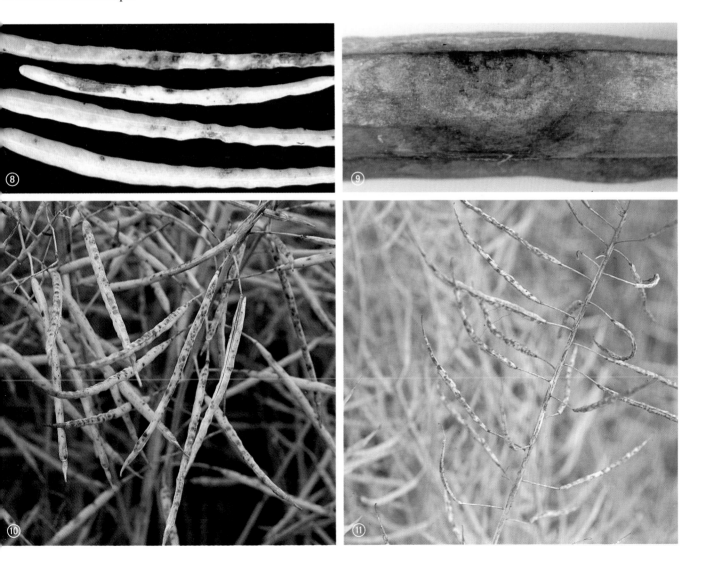

Grey Mould *Botrytis cinerea* Pers. – *Botryotinia fuckeliana*

Causal Organism and Symptoms

Grey mould disease, also called Botrytis stem rot, is caused by the fungus *Botrytis cinerea* Pers. (sexual stage: *Botryotinia fuckeliana* [de Bary] Whetzel).

The first visible symptoms are usually greyish-white lesions on older plant parts or senescent leaves ❶, ❷. Subsequently these can spread over the whole leaf which yellows and dies. Passing down the petiole the pathogen penetrates the stem ❸, ❼ producing oval-shaped, grey-brown lesions several centimeters long ❽. In advanced stages these lesions girdle the stem ❹, ❺, ❽ and might be confused with symptoms caused by *Sclerotinia sclerotiorum* stem rot . However, grey mould usually leaves the pith intact with no sclerotia although microsclerotia sometimes occur ❾. Early attacks may cause stunting ❹ and premature ripening ('whiteheads'). Distal parts of affected racemes lose their green colour, lodge and die ❻, ❿.

Infected pods are covered with light brown spots which under high humidity, produce a characteristic sporulating grey brown mycelium ❿, ⓫. Pods attacked during the early stage of formation are stunted and will shatter if repeated changes of humid and dry weather occur.

Biology

B. cinerea is a very common fungus, but its biology on rape has not yet been much studied. For example, the reasons are not known why only a few individual stems are attacked despite sufficient spores being produced on the diseased plants to cause epidemic spread of the disease. Cool and humid seasons, poor crop aeration, frost damage and early lodging, all favour the disease.

Host Range

The host range of *B. cinerea* is vast and includes many vegetable, ornamental, field and fruit crops, especially annuals.

Occurrence and Importance

The fungus is ubiquitous. Incidence on oilseed rape may be significant in humid seasons and in certain protected sites. Yield losses can be expected from severe stem or pod attacks, but there is no reliable information on losses.

Literature
Coley-Smith, J. R., Verhoeff, K. & Jarvis, W. R., 1980: The biology of *Botrytis*. Academic Press, London.

Typhula Root Rot *Typhula gyrans* (Batsch) Fr.

Causal Organism and Symptoms

The disease is caused by the soilborne fungus *Typhula gyrans* (Batsch) Fr.

Infected or dead plants occur singly or in patches ❶, ❷ at the end of winter, after snow has melted away. The shoot tips and stalks of the older leaves are shrunken and frequently covered with a white mycelium. The leaves and stalks undergo a yellowish to red discolouration and finally dry out and die. Initially, the root remains intact or is only slightly affected. Infected plants are covered with the mycelium and rape seed sized resting bodies (sclerotia) of the fungus ❸, ❹, ❺, ❻. These are firstly yellow and then dark brown, finally black. Distinction from the resting forms of other sclerotia-forming fungi is possible by their different size and shape.

Usually affected plants do no survive and will die by the end o spring.

Biology

The life cycle of *T. gyrans* on oilseed rape is not yet fully elucidated. Frequently the fungus attacks plants which have been covered by snow for a long time. Under these conditions of low light and high humidity fungal growth is favoured. There is some evidence that *T. gyrans* attacks occur most frequently on plants which have previously been damaged by other causes. The sclerotia of the fungus survive for several years in the soil and are the main source of infections.

Host Range

The host range of *T. gyrans* is not yet well known.

Occurrence and Importance

Typhula rot is usually limited to plants which have suffered from a harsh winter and long periods of snow cover. Damage is in most cases not consistent and often affects only single plants. In certain sites where patches of diseased plants occur there may be appreciable yield losses.

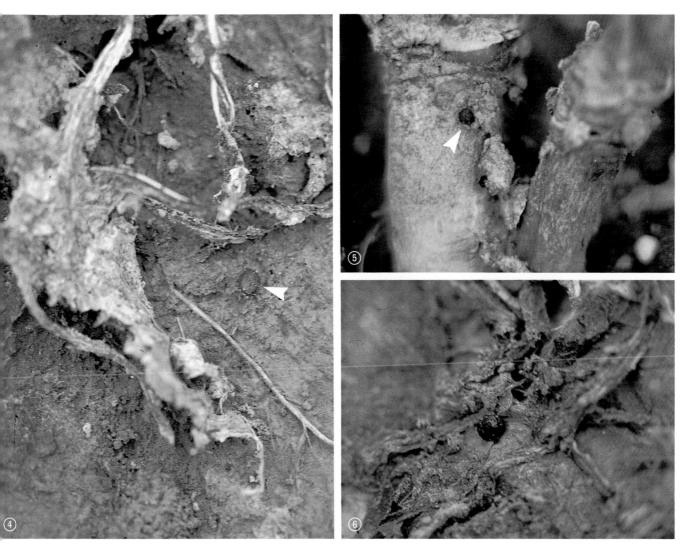

Verticillium Wilt *Verticillium dahliae* Kleb.

Causal Organism and Symptoms

Verticillium wilt also called stem rot, is caused by the soil-borne fungus *Verticillium dahliae* Kleb. On single plants the first symptoms appear from the time of flowering onward, initially as a yellowing and later bronzing of one side of the leaves ❷, ❸, ❹, ❽.

The main roots of carefully removed plants show grey to blue-black streaks ⓫ while the lateral roots have frequently completely decayed so that the plants are pulled out with ease. This contrasts with plants affected by *Phoma lingam* stem canker where the lateral roots remain intact. Generally the disease appears only during matu-

ration of the crop and on stubble after harvest. On one side of the stem there are frequently characteristic light brown streaks corresponding to infected xylem vessels beneath ❺, ❻, ❿. The tissues situated between the attacked vessels collapse and shrivel. Attacked plants ripen prematurely ⓭ and sometimes lodge ❶, ❼. The stem

base and roots become dark grey to black ❾, the fungus having produced abundant subepidermal resting bodies (microsclerotia). Sometimes microsclerotia also form on the surface of tissues and affected plants become dark grey. The stem tissues appear as if they were sprinkled with iron filings and the vessels within are also greyish

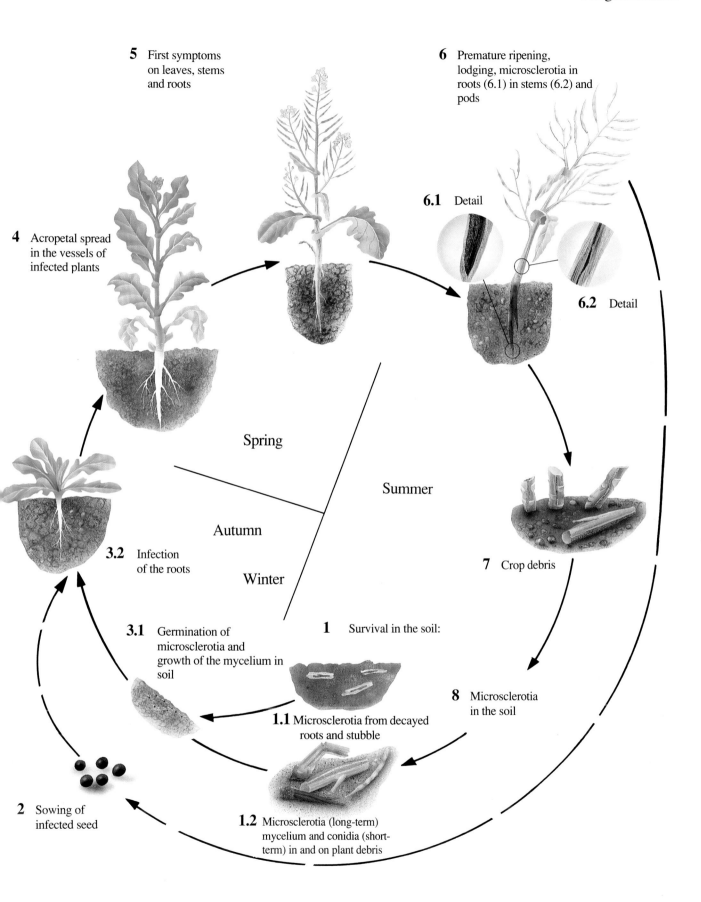

5 First symptoms on leaves, stems and roots

6 Premature ripening, lodging, microsclerotia in roots (6.1) in stems (6.2) and pods

6.1 Detail

4 Acropetal spread in the vessels of infected plants

6.2 Detail

Spring

Summer

3.2 Infection of the roots

Autumn

Winter

7 Crop debris

3.1 Germination of microsclerotia and growth of the mycelium in soil

1 Survival in the soil:

8 Microsclerotia in the soil

1.1 Microsclerotia from decayed roots and stubble

2 Sowing of infected seed

1.2 Microsclerotia (long-term) mycelium and conidia (short-term) in and on plant debris

black ❿, ⓬, ⓴. Later the cuticle peels off in small strips.

Some of the external symptoms of wilt are similar to those produced by *P. lingam* or *S. sclerotiorum.*

Biology

At harvest the asexually formed resting bodies (microsclerotia) (1.1) of *V. dahliae* fall onto the soil (7, 8) where they remain viable and infective for several years (1). Swedish studies have demonstrated severe Verticillium attacks on fields which had not grown oilseed rape for the preceding 8 to 10 years.

Mycelium from these propagules is the main source of infection which begins on roots of young plants. Conidia on verticillately-branched conidiophores are rarely produced on host surfaces so contribute little to disease spread.

Although infection may be initiated very early in autumn (3.2) the first symptoms are usually not seen until late spring.

The pathogen, like some other vascular diseases, spreads in the vascular tissue (4) of infected plants and produces wilting (5) and stem drying symptoms only in advanced stages of pathogenesis. Premature ripening (6) and sometimes early lodging are the most apparent symptoms.Microsclerotia (6, 7) are found outside as well as inside the stem, in contrast with the fruiting bodies (pycnidia) of

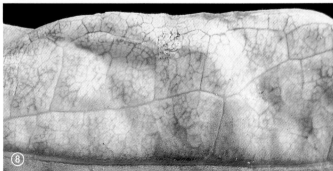

homa lingam which are similar in shape and size but found nly in the outer cell layers. Anher, but less important, source f infection is contamination of eds produced in side severely fected pods (2).

ost Range

V. dahliae attacks an exemely wide range of annual and perennial species of wild and cultivated dicotyledons, e.g. some species of Solanaceae, Cucurbitaceae, Malvaceae, Rosaceae and Compositae.

Occurrence and Importance

Rape wilt has caused yield losses in Sweden and east and west Germany. In Sweden, the disease is considered the most injurious to oilseed rape. Yield losses up to 50% may occur in regions where rape has been cultivated for long periods or where it is frequent in rotations. The increase in the area cropped with rape in the last decade is likely to favour a further spread of the disease, even in regions where until now is has not been a problem.

Literature

Svensson, Ch. and Lerenius, C. 1987: An investigation on the effect of *Verticillium Wilt (Verticillium dahliae* Kleb.) on oilseed rape 10 BC Working Group Integrated Control in Oilseed Rape. West Palaeartic Regional Section Bulletin, **4**, 30–34.

Woolliams, G.E., 1966: Host range and symptomatology of *Verticillium dahliae* in economic, weed and native plants in interior British Columbia, Canadian Journal of Plant Science, **46**, 661–669

Light Leaf Spot *Cylindrosporium concentricum* Grev. – *Pyrenopeziza brassicae*

Causal Organism and Symptoms

Light leaf spot is caused by of the fungus *Cylindrosporium concentricum* Grev. The sexual stage of the fungus, *Pyrenopeziza brassicae* Sutton & Rawlinson, is rarely reported, but apothecia occur on the decaying petioles of fallen leaves among crop debris on the soil surface ⓳.

First symptoms are usually seen from January onwards, though latent infection is commonly initiated in autumn. Very small white spots ❷, ❸ caused by spore masses (acervuli) of the fungus erupting through the cuticle can occur on both surfaces of leaves. Subsequently the single lesions coalesce and the whole leaf may be killed ❶. Frequently the leaf surface is malformed and the cuticle is broken ❹. Severe attacks may cause falciform ❻ distortion of the leaf. Leaves which have been completely necrosed often do not absciss but remain attached to the stem ❼, ⓮.

On stems and lateral branches there may be superficial, elongated, fawn lesions with black speckling at the edges ⓾, ⓭, ⓬ which, in conditions of high humidity, are later surrounded by

white spore masses. The epidermis of these lesions is often repeatedly broken transversely **9**, **10**, **11**, **12**, **13**. Lesions are also formed on the lower stem and might be confused with those caused by *Phoma lingam*.

Affected buds **8** and pods are covered with small, white to fawn spots which later coalesce so that the whole pod is discoloured **16**, **17**. If the attack is very severe, the whole raceme may become brown, or the pods themselves may be curled and distorted **16**, **18**. The pedicels may be lesioned and transversely split. Pod damage can lead to premature ripening and pod shattering.

Biology

The fungus survives on crop debris (1) which is the main source of infection. Conidia produced on the debris are transported by wind-borne rain and may infect young plants before winter (2.1). Transmission by infected seed is possible but there are no reports about its importance for the spread of the

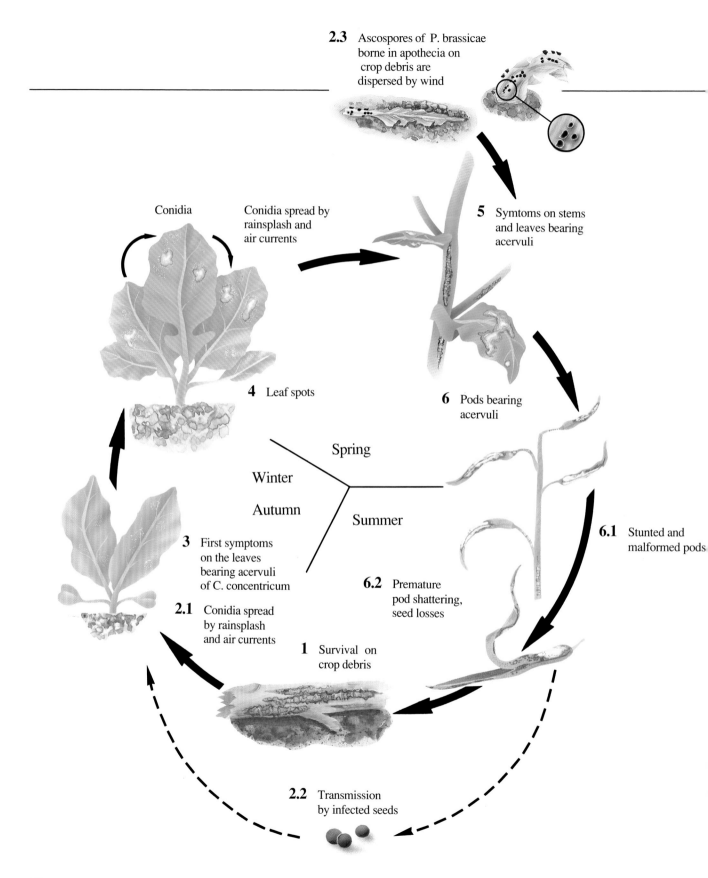

2.3 Ascospores of P. brassicae
borne in apothecia on
crop debris are
dispersed by wind

Conidia

Conidia spread by
rainsplash and
air currents

5 Symtoms on stems
and leaves bearing
acervuli

4 Leaf spots

6 Pods bearing
acervuli

Spring

Winter

Autumn

Summer

6.1 Stunted and
malformed pods

3 First symptoms
on the leaves
bearing acervuli
of C. concentricum

6.2 Premature
pod shattering,
seed losses

2.1 Conidia spread
by rainsplash
and air currents

1 Survival on
crop debris

2.2 Transmission
by infected seeds

isease (2.2). Infection spreads o new leaves and other plants y conidia produced in specialed subcuticular bodies (aceruli) (3, 4, 5, 6) on the plants riginally infected in autumn.

High humidity favours pread of the disease. Particulary severe attacks occur when a ool wet autumn is followed by mild humid winter and a wet

spring up to May. The unicellular conidia released after prolonged humid periods are transported by rain splash over short distances and further by windborne droplets. In favourable conditions (temperatures between 5 and 15 °C) the spores germinate and infect the aerial parts of oilseed rape within five days. After invading the plant

the fungus grows subcuticularly until breaking through to give the described symptoms. It is well able to survive winters under snow cover.

Ascospores are produced from apothecia on crop debris from spring through to autumn. Ascospore release is associated with rain, most being released after rainfall when the crop de-

bris is wet. The airborne spores have the potential to travel considerable distances on the wind to infect other crops. Their role in the life cycle and dispersal of *P. brassicae* has been proposed (2.3), but it is not yet known how important they are in the development of an epidemic under field conditions.

Host Range

C. concentricum attacks only *Brassica* species. All major forms of cultivated brassicas are potential hosts.

Occurrence and Importance

Light leaf spot is a major disease causing significant yield loss in rape in Britain and northern France and, recently, in some parts of Germany. It occurs in Sweden, Poland and to a lesser extent elsewhere in western Europe.

Literature

McCartney, H. A. & Lacey, M. E., 1989: The production and dispersal of ascospores of *Pyrenopeziza brassicae* in oilseed rape. Aspects of Applied Biology **23**, 401-408.

McCartney, H. A., Lacey, M. E. & Rawlinson, C. J., 1989: The perfect stage of *Pyrenopeziza brassicae* on oilseed rape and its agricultural implications. 7th Intern. Rapeseed Congress, Poznan proceedings **5**, 1262–1267.

Paul, V. H., Burhenne, S, Günzelmann ⁄ und Masuch, G., 1980: Zur Bedeutur von *Pyrenopeziza brassicae* für da Auftreten der Cylindrosporiose im Wir terraps in Deutschl. Raps, **8** (3), 172–17.

Penaud,A.,1987: La maladie des tache blanches du colza. Phytoma, 23–26

Rawlinson, C. J., Sutton, B. C. & Muthy alv G.,1978: Taxonomy and biology ⁄ *Pyrenopeziza brassicae* sp. nov. *(Cy concentricum)*, a pathogen of winter c seed rape *(Brassica napus* ssp. *oleifera* Trans Br. Mycol. Soc. **71**, 425-439.

White Leaf Spot *Pseudocercosporella capsellae* (Ell. & Ev.) Deighton

Causal Organism and Symptoms

White leaf spot is caused by the fungus *Pseudocercosporella capsellae* (Ell. & Ev.) Deighton which attacks leaves, stems and pods of oilseed rape.

First signs of infection on leaves are small (1 to 2 mm in diameter) fawn to bronze coloured spots, which later enlarge to 0.5 to 1.5 cm and become white or grey at the center with a dark green to purple or brown margin ❶, ❷, ❸, ❹. Numerous spores (conidia) are produced at the centre of lesions and sometimes the necrotic tissues may break. Severe attacks with coalescing lesions leads to early necrosis and abscission of the whole leaf.

Stems have fawn, elongated, slightly sunken lesions with a wide dark brown margin. Lesions spread up and down the stem and are then grey with purple-brown margins giving a speckled appearance ❺, ❻.

On pods there are fawn to grey, slightly sunken lesions with a wide brown-black margin and central speckling produced by the small greyish hyphal masses of the fungus (stromata) ❼, ❽, ❾, ❿.

The symptoms are easily confused with some of those produced by *Phoma, Cylindrosporium, Alternaria* and *Verticillium*.

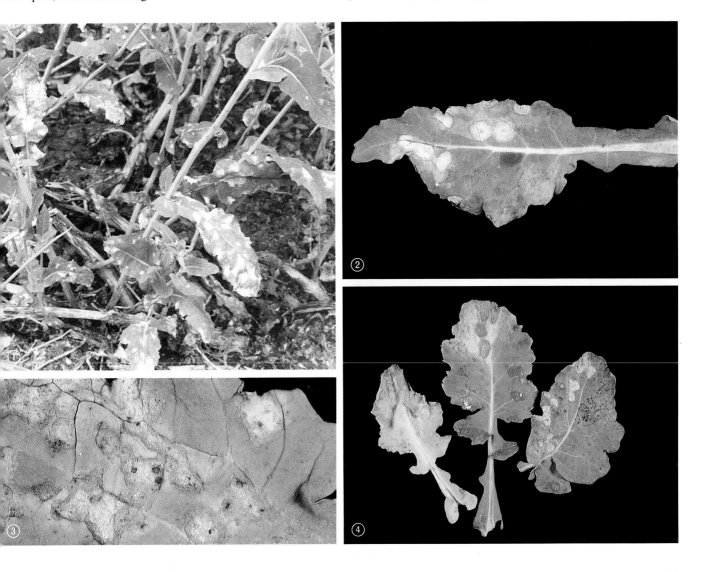

Biology

In the absence of a sexual stage survival has been attributed to thick walled dark mycelium (stromata) on crop debris (1.1). This stromata can remain viable for at least nine months and may produce conidia which infect rape crops (2.1, 3.1). A sexual stage has recently been discovered and named *Mycosphaerella capsellae* sp. nov. Inman & Sivanesan (1.2). Airborne ascospores are now considered to be the main source of primary inoculum for infecting autumn-sown crops (1.2, 2.2, 3.2). Secondary spread during winter, spring and summer is by dary conidia formed on the attacked tissues which show the typical symptoms of the disease (5, 6, 7). The spores are spread locally by rainsplash and over longer distances by wind-blown rain. Persistent rain and temperatures between 14 and 20 °C favour the development of the disease. Under these conditions first symptoms on susceptible oilseed rape cultivars are produced in about a week.

Host Range

Many other species of cruciferae are hosts of the pathogen e.g. mustard, swede cabbage and stubble turnip. Affected weed species which may provide an additional source of infection are shepherd's purse, charlock and wild radish.

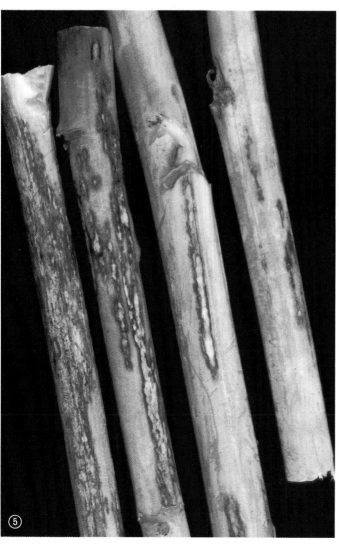

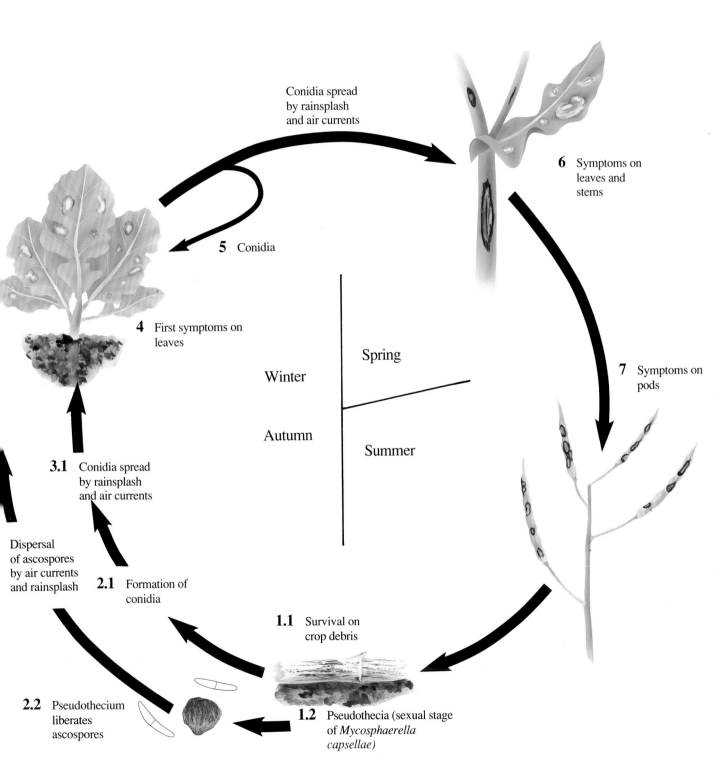

Conidia spread
by rainsplash
and air currents

6 Symptoms on
leaves and
stems

5 Conidia

4 First symptoms on
leaves

Spring

Winter

Autumn

Summer

7 Symptoms on
pods

3.1 Conidia spread
by rainsplash
and air currents

Dispersal
of ascospores
by air currents
and rainsplash

2.1 Formation of
conidia

1.1 Survival on
crop debris

2.2 Pseudothecium
liberates
ascospores

1.2 Pseudothecia (sexual stage
of *Mycosphaerella
capsellae*)

Occurrence and Importance

Damage to rape by *P. capsellae* has been recorded in southern England, in Canada and in Australia. In eastern Germany the disease was reported for the first time in 1986. Severe damage has been reported from France, but there is little information about its effect on yield.

Literature

Amelung, D. und Daebeler F., 1988: Die Weißfleckenkrankheit *(Pseudocercosporella capsellae* [Ell. et Ev.] Deighton) – eine in der DDR neue Krankheit am Winterraps. Nachrichtenbl. Pflanzenschutzd. DDR, 42 (4), 73–74.

Anon, 1980: Commonwealth Mycological Institute.Distribution Maps of Plant Diseases: *Pseudocercos. capsellae,* No. 197.

Campbell, R. N. & Greathead, A. S.1978: *Pseudocercosporella* white spot of crucifers in California. Plant Disease Reporter **62**, 1066-1068.

Crosnan, D. F. 1954: Cercosporella leaf spot of crucifers. North Carolina Agricultural Experimental Station Technical Bulletin l09, 23p.

Davis, W. H., 1927: *Cercosporella* leaf-spot of Chinese cabbage in Massachusetts. Phytopathology **17**, 669–671.

Deighton, F. C., 1973: Studies on *Cercospora* and allied genera IV. Mycological Papers **133**, 42–46.

Fitt, B. D. L., Dhua, U., Lacey, M. E. and McCartney, H. A., 1989: Effects of leaf age and position on splash dispersal of *Pseudocercosporella capsellae*, cause of white leaf spot on oilseed rape. Aspects Applied Biology **23**, 457–464.

Hardwick, N. V., Culshaw, F. A., Davic J. M. L., Gladders, P., Hawkins, J. H. ar Slawson, D. D. 1989: Incidence and s verity of fungal diseases of oilseed rape England and Wales, 1986–1988. Aspec of Applied Biology **23**, 383-400.

Inman, A. J., Sivanesan, A., Fitt, B.D. and Evans, R. L. 1991: The biology of *M. cosphaerella capsellae* sp. nov., the tele morph of *Pseudocercosporella capsella* cause of white leaf spot of oilseed rape Mycological Research **95**, 1334–1342.

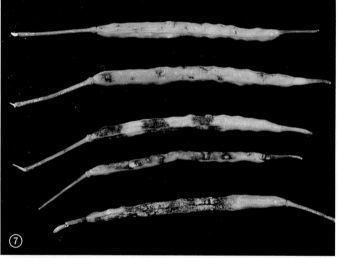

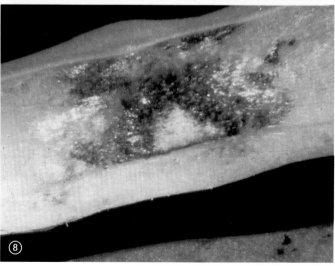

Ramularia Leaf Spot *Ramularia armoraciae* Fuckel

Causal Organism and Symptoms

The disease is caused by the fungus *Ramularia armoraciae* Fuckel.

Small light brown lesions of irregular shape and with a more less well defined brown margin occur on leaves.

In severe attacks the older leaves may absciss prematurely.

Occurrence and Importance

R. amoraciae has been recorded on male-sterile lines of rape in France, but rarely on rape elsewhere, although it causes a white spot of horseradish throughout Europe.

Literature
Brun, H., Renard, M., Jouan, B., Tanguy, X. & Lamarque, C., 1979: Observations préliminaires sur quelques maladies du colza en France: *Sclerotinia sclerotiorum, Cylindrosporium concentricum, Ramularia amoraciae*. Science Agronomique Rennes (1979), 7–77.

White Rust *Albugo candida* (Pers.) Kuntze

Causal Organism and Symptoms

The disease is caused by the fungus *Albugo candida* (Pers.) Kuntze.

Leaves, shoots, buds, flowers and pods can be affected and covered with white, chalky, blister-like pustules. Thickened, fawn flecks occur on the upper surface of the leaves with whitish pustules on the corresponding lower surface. Infected racemes may be malformed and hypertrophied. Systemic infection of the inflorescence gives rise to galls known as 'stagheads'.

Biology

The fungus is not, as the common name might suggest, a rust fungus but a species of the lower fungi Oomycetes. Survival is by oospores in decaying crop debris. Primary infections are from zoospores arising from oospores; secondary spread is by airborne sporangia that release zoospores on host surfaces. On some hosts the fungus commonly occurs in close association with *Peronospora parasitica*, both fungi causing staghead galls by simultaneous infection.

Occurrence and Importance

The fungus occurs on many cruciferous hosts, including cultivated *Brassica* species and radish, but in Europe the disease has rarely been observed on oilseed rape.

It is more common on rape in Canada and India.

Literature
Harper, F. R. and U. J. Pittman; 1974: Yield loss by *Brassica campestris* and *B. napus* from systemic stem infection by *Albugo cruciferarum*. Phytopathology, **64**, 408-410.
Verma P. R., Harding H., Petrie G. A., Williams, P, H., 1975: Infection and temporal development of mycelium of *Albugo candida* in cotyledons of four *Brassica* species. Canadian Journal of Botany **53**, 1016–1020.

Ring Spot *Mycosphaerella brassicicola* (Duby) Lindau

Causal Organism and Symptoms

Ring spot disease is caused by the fungus *Mycosphaerella brassicicola* (Duby) Lindau and its asexual stage *Asteromella brassicae* (Chev.) Boerema & van Kest. Attacked leaves are covered with fawn to dark brown, slightly sunken spots of varying size with a thin, definite brownblack margin. Later the single spots may coalesce and extend to the whole leaf which dies ❶, ❷. Affected tissues are covered with very small black fruiting bodies (spermagonia and pseudothecia) forming concentric rings. The fruiting bodies are similar in shape and colour to those of *Phoma lingam* but smaller.

Affected stems and pods show similar symptoms ❸, ❹, ❺. The disease may be confused with white leaf spot *(P. capsellae)*, stem canker *(P. lingam)* or light leaf spot *(C. concentricum)*.

Biology

The fungus produces asexual and later sexual fruiting bodies with spores. Infected tissues initially produce spermagonia containing spermatia and the pseudothecia with sexual ascospores. The latter, over wintering on the remnants of the vegetation, are the source of primary infection in spring. Single spermatia are not viable and are not able to cause primary infections in spring. Spores ar

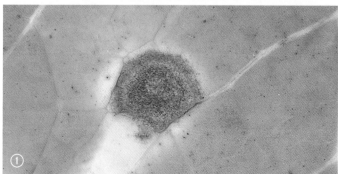

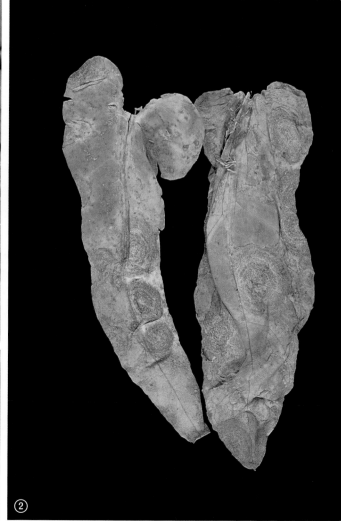

...read by air currents and rain. ...ong periods of high humidity, ...in and temperatures hetween ...5 and 20 °C favour the development of epidemics.

...ost Range

...Ring spot has been recorded ...n most Brassica crops and on ...ild crucifers like shepherd's ...urse.

Occurrence and Importance

Occurrence on rape can be significant on sites where kale or cabbage is cultivated in the neighbourhood or are in the same crop rotation. Economic importance has not yet been well studied but seems to be minor in Europe.

Literature

Dring, D. M., 1961: Studies on *Mycosphaerella brassicicola* (Duby) Oudem. Transactions of the British Mycological Society **44**, 253-264.

Nelson, M. R. & Pound, G. S., 1959: The relation of environment to the ringspot (*Mycosphaerella brassicicola*) disease of crucifers. Phytopathology **49**, 633-640.

Snyder, W. C., 1946: Spermogonia versus pycnidia in *Mycosphaerella brassicicola*. Phytopathology **36**, 481-484.

Vanterpool, T. C., 1969: Overwintering and spread of *Mycosphaerella brassicicola*, the cause of ringspot of rape. Proceedings of the Canadian Phytopathological Society **36**, 20.

Weimer, J. L., 1926: Ringspot of crucifers caused by *Mycosphaerella brassicicola*. Journal of Agricultural Research **32**, 97-132.

Zornbach, W., 1989: personal communication.

④

⑤

Sore Shin & Damping off *Rhizoctonia solani* Kühn

Causal Organism and Symptoms

Sore shin on rape is caused by the fungus *Rhizoctonia solani* Kühn with its perfect stage known as *Thanatephorus cucumeris* (Frank) Donck.

Well defined dark brown coloured lesions with a light grey center occur on the stem base. They are up to 4 cm long and of irregular, angular or ellipsoidal shape, rarely girdling the stem and very clearly distinguished from the healthy tissues ❶, ❷. The symptoms are quite similar to those produced on affected cereals by *R. cerealis*. Usually only superficial tissues undergo dry rot. Sometimes the attacked tissues appear lacerated and fibrous and the whole stem base may rot ❸, ❹, but this is rare.

Another symptom on the stem base could be termed 'white collar'. This occurs after long periods in standing water when the stem base becomes covered with a waxy pellicle of white and sometimes grey mycelium while the cortical tissues remain intact ❺.

On seedlings and on the roots of older plants elongate, brown lesions cause soft rot or girdling of the attacked parts. The seedlings fall over and die, hence the names 'seedling blight' or 'damping off' given to this complex of symptoms, which may also be caused by *Phoma lingam* or species of *Alternaria, Pythium* and *Fusarium.*

Biology

R. solani is an aggregate species containing fungi with widely varied morphology and pathology attacking a vast range of cultivated and wild plants: some 250 species in about 60 families. Single isolates of different origin may differ in host range and pathogenicity.

Occurrence and Importance

The fungus is almost ubiquitous in cultivated soils. Sore shin has been only occasionally observed in oilseed rape and is condered a minor problem. East German studies report, for certain sites, an average incidence of about 20% at the time of swathing. In one case nearly 90% of the plants were affected. The disease was very common in 1988 and caused, in some cases, complete rot of the stem base. The most damaging infections are probably those on the roots of older plants.

Literature

Daebeler, F., 1989: personal communication.

Daebeler, F., Amelung, D. und Engel, K.-H., 1985: – Zur Verwechslungsmöglichkeit der durch *Phoma lingam* (Tode ex Fr.) Desm. verursachten Wurzelhalsfäule mit *Rhizoctonia solani* K. und *Verticillium dahliae* Kleb. – Nachrichtenbl. Pflanzenschutz d. e. DDR **39**, (9), 180-181.

Gugel, R. K., Yitbarek, S. M., Verma, R. A. A., Morall and Sadasivaiah, R. S., 1987: Etiology of the rhizoctonia root rot complex of canola in the Peace River region of Alberta. Canadian Journal of Plant Pathology **9**, 119–128.

Raabe, A., 1939: – Untersuchungen über pilzparasitäre Krankheiten von Raps und Rüben.–Cbl. Bak. u. Parasitenkd. II **100**, 35–52.

Tewari, J. P., Cahman, A. I. and Furuya, H., 1987: Pathogens of the seedling blight of Canola in Alberta.–7th International Rapeseed Congress, Poznan–Poland 11–14 May 1987. Abstracts, 255.

Pests

Slugs

Reticulated Field Slug *Deroceras reticulatum Müll.*

Deroceras reticulatum is about 50 - 65 mm long and of yellowish - white, grey, or reddish - brown colour with nearly black spots and a netlike pattern on the back.

Deroceras agreste is yellowish - white or grey coloured and smaller than the previous species without dark spots or patterns on the back.

On attacked plants, the cotyledons may be severed and the foliage leaves irregularly perforated with signs of nibbling at their margins while the principal veins remain intact ❶, ❷, ❸. Slime tracks left by the slugs are usually seen on the plant and on the soil. In dry weather slugs are found only at night on plants, while in very humid or rainy conditions they may be active also early in the morning or in the evening.

Biology

Field slugs are hermaphrodites and, following reciprocal copulation during spring to autumn, both partners lay groups of 10 to 30 glassy eggs, 2 mm in diameter, in the soil or on decaying plant parts ❹. The young slugs which hatch three to four weeks after oviposition will be sexually mature after another six weeks and live about six to eight months. Normally the winter period is passed as an egg, but sometimes adults may survive winter. Field slug populations increase after warm winters and in humid seasons bu

Grey Field Slug *Deroceras agreste L.*

nd to decrease in dry, hot sum-
ers.

Host Range

Field slugs are not specialised
n certain hosts and cause dam-
ge to young and tender tissues
f many plant species such as
ubble turnip, cabbage, cereals,
aize and potatoes.

Occurrence and Importance

Both species are widespread.
Slugs are regarded as important
pests of rape in Belgium, France
and Germany; *D. reticulatum*
occurs mainly in southern and
central Germany and *D. agreste*
is more common in the northern
parts of the country. They are
minor pests of rape in Britain,
but recently severe damage has
been caused on low - glucosinolate cultivars.

Slug damage on oilseed rape
can be expected in humid seasons or in moist microclimates,
especially where debris has ac-
cumulated after harvesting, and
sometimes it has been necessary
to plough down the whole crop.

Threshold

The threshold for control is
not yet established.

Natural Enemies

Slug populations are normally controlled by predators such
as carabid beetles, toads, hedge-
hogs and other polyphagous
species.

Beetles and Weevils

Cabbage Stem Flea Beetle *Psylliodes chrysocephala L.*

Organism and Symptoms

The adult beetles are blue - black, 3 - 4.5 mm long ❶; sometimes individuals are seen with light brown elytra. The adults jump using specialised saltatory legs with swollen hind femurs. The creamy white larvae have numerous dark spots on the back and are up to 7 mm long. They have three pairs of thoracic legs and a dark brown head ❺.

The adults feed on the cotyledons and on the first leaves causing typical round holes with the upper or lower epidermis of the leaf remaining intact (window feeding) ❸; occasionally complete perforation ('shot-holing') occurs ❷, ❸.

The damage caused by the larvae is economically much more important. Larvae penetrate and mine the older petioles ❹. Later they migrate to the stem of the plant and can damage the growing point ❺, ❻.

Biology

The adults appear in late June or in July feeding on maturing pods and stems (1). After this they move to moist and shaded places for their summer diapause (2).

At the beginning of September the beetles return (3) to feed on the young rape plants (4). After two weeks of feeding the females lay their eggs in the upper layers of the soil near rape plants (5). The period of oviposition may last until spring if winter is mild and thus it is possible to find eggs, larvae and adults at the same time. The lar-

vae hatch in late autumn or spring and migrate to the ho plants penetrating into the pe oles (6) then moving to the ste and growing point (7). In la spring the mature larvae leav the plants and pupate in the so (8, 9). Sometimes the first pupa are seen before winter althoug this is not usual in Britain. Th beetle completes one generatio in each year.

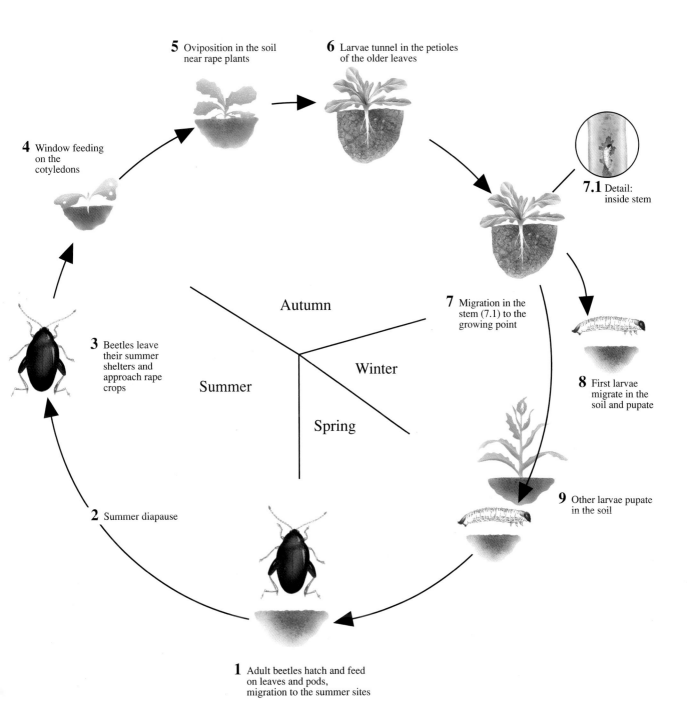

5 Oviposition in the soil near rape plants

6 Larvae tunnel in the petioles of the older leaves

4 Window feeding on the cotyledons

7.1 Detail: inside stem

3 Beetles leave their summer shelters and approach rape crops

Autumn

Winter

Summer

Spring

7 Migration in the stem (7.1) to the growing point

8 First larvae migrate in the soil and pupate

2 Summer diapause

9 Other larvae pupate in the soil

1 Adult beetles hatch and feed on leaves and pods, migration to the summer sites

Host Range

Numerous wild crucifers such as wild mustard, shepherd's purse and wild radish are attacked.

Occurrence and Importance

Cabbage stem flea beetle is a common pest in some areas of Britain and France and in northern Germany and less common in the south of Germany.

Window feeding damage on the leaves is rarely injurious; the main damage is caused by the larvae. The tunnels in the petioles are easily filled with water which, when frozen, can cause severe over - winter loss of plants. Further damage may result from fungi such as *Phoma lingam* and *Verticillium dahliae* (the causal agents of stem canker and of wilt) which use larval lesions as infection sites.

Some other species of flea beetle, e.g. cabbage flea beetle (*Phyllotreta* spp.), whose larvae feed on cabbages, are usually not injurious to winter oilseed rape, but can damage spring rape if seed is not treated.

Threshold

1) Adults, attacks on seedlings and on young plants:
   - 10% of total leaf surface destroyed
2) Adults, attacks on plants having more than four leaves:
   a) -1 beetle/m2
   b) yellow dish traps (provisional threshold)
      – well developed crops: 10 beetles /24 h / trap exceeded on several occasions
      – poorly developed crops: 5 beetles /24 h / trap exceeded on several occasions
3) Larvae (provisional threshold): - 3 to 5 larvae / plant, varying with plant development.

Natural Enemies

Cabbage stem flea beetle attacked by parasitic soil inhabiting nematodes and by some species of Hymenoptera.

iterature

allanger, Y. ,1984: Observations agrologiques sur l'altise d'hiver du colzu *Psylliodes chrysocephala L.).* Thèse de octeur Ingénieur, INA P. G . Paris, 167

onnemaison, L. & Jourdheuil, P., 1954: 'altise d'hiver du colza *(Psylliodes hrysocephala* L.). Ann. INRA série C, **8,** 45-524.

ossfeld, R., 1987: Schadensschwellen ei tierischen Rapsschädlingen. Raps, 5. g. (2), 70-72.

John, M. E., & Holliday, J. M., 1984: Distribution and chemical control of *Psylliodes chrysocephala* and *Ceutorhynchus picitarsis* in winter oilseed rape. Aspects of Applied Biology 6, 281–292.

Schulz, R.-R., 1985: Untersuchungen zur Vermehrungsrate des Rapserdflohs *(Psylliodes chrysocephala* L.). Arch. Phytopathol. Pflanzenschutz, Berlin **21** (4), 305-311.

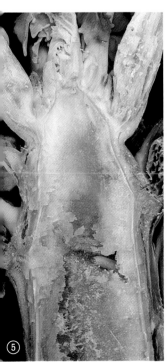

Turnip Gall Weevil *Ceutorhynchus pleurostigma Marsh.*

Organism and Symptoms

The turnip gall weevil, sometimes called cabbage gall weevil, is 2 - 3 mm long and grey in colour. The creamy white larvae are legless.

The main roots or root collars of attacked plants have one or more smooth, hemispherical galls about 1 cm in diameter ❶, ❷. Transverse sections of the galls clearly show the larvae and their feeding tunnels ❸, ❹ which facilitates their distinction from club root galls caused by *P. brassicae*.

The galls are excavated by the larvae in the course of their development.

Biology

The adult weevils pass summer in diapause and attack plants of oilseed rape early in autumn. After maturation feeding the female starts to lay single eggs into the root collar cortex or, if the soil is sufficiently friable, into the root. Each larva causes the development of a single gall. The mature larvae leave the galls in spring and pupate in an earthen cocoon several centimeters deep in soil. The adults hatch after six to eight weeks and then pass summer in diapause. The turnip gall weevil completes only one generation each year, but there are summer and winter types: The first type overwinters as a larva while the latter passes winter as an adult

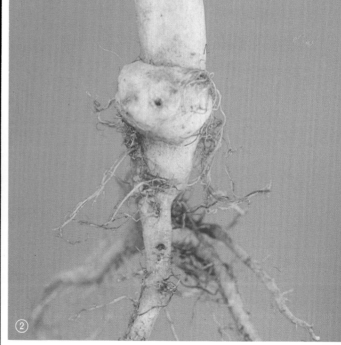

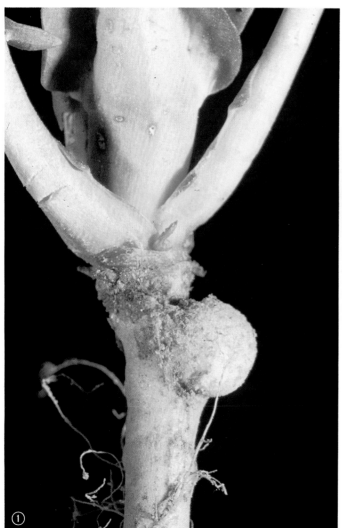

…eevil and begins oviposition in …pring only, thus being less injurious than the summer type.

Host Range

The host range of the turnip gall weevil includes various other species of crucifer such as cabbage, swede, turnip, radish, wild mustard and wild radish.

Occurrence and Importance

The turnip gall weevil is seldom injurious to oilseed rape, although the crop may serve as a reservoir of the pest. Locally, severe attacks may enhance overwinter losses of plants or favour penetration by agents of fungal stem rot diseases.

Threshold

None at present, treatment seldom necessary.

Literature
Schneiding, U., 1956: Untersuchungen zur Biologie des Kohlgallenrüßlers *Ceutorynchus pleurostigma* Marsham. Z. Angew. Entomol **39**, 186-228.

Rape Stem Weevil *Ceutorhynchus napi Gyll.*

Organism and Symptoms

Rape stem weevils are 3.2 - 4 mm long and covered with grey hairs such that a slate grey colour is produced ❶. The head is lengthened into a thin downward curved proboscis and the legs are black. The larvae are legless and yellowy white in colour with a dark brown head later turning light brown ❹. On being disturbed the adults drop to the ground and remain there motionless so that it is quite difficult to find weevils on plants.

The first symptoms of attack are shiny and later white - bordered punctures on the stem, frequently near the growing point ❶, ❸. During stem extension the lesions are stretched forming thin grooves, thickenings and malformations mostly on the lower parts of the stem ❻, ❼, ❽. It is there that the stems later burst and roll outward ❺, ❿ especially after heavy rains or frost. The penetration of water and of pathogenic fungi may cause secondary rotting of the stem base. The exit holes of larvae which leave the stems, usually at the point of insertion of petioles, are found later ❽, ❾. The affected plants produce many lateral branches and their flowering is prolonged.

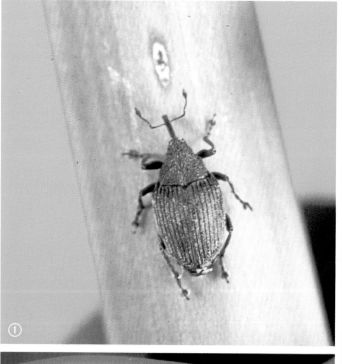

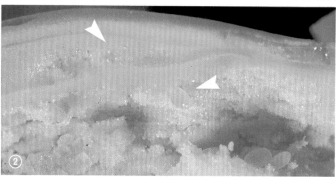

Biology

The fully developed adults remain in the cocoon and over-winter in the soil (6). As soon as the soil temperature has reached 5 °C to 7 °C at a depth of 2 cm (corresponding to daily mean air temperatures of 10 °C to 12 °C) the weevils fly to new rape crops (1, 2). After two weeks of maturation feeding the female begins oviposition on the upper parts of the stem (3) ❷ causing small blister - like malformations (4). The larvae feed in the pith of the stem until maturation ❿ and then leave the plants to pupate in the soil (5). The young weevils hatch in autumn but do not leave the exuviae (6) until spring. In the climate of Continental Europe the weevil completes one generation each year.

Host Range

The rape stem weevil attacks other cultivated brassicas and wild crucifers.

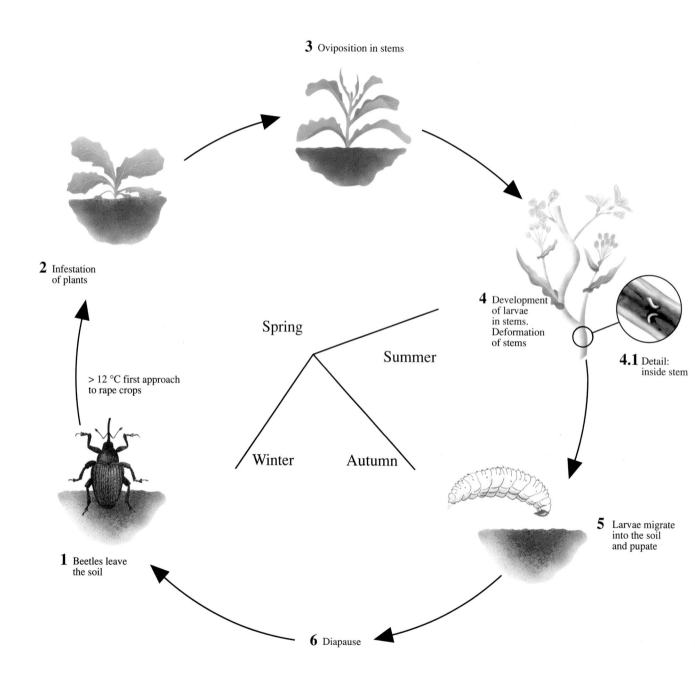

3 Oviposition in stems

2 Infestation
of plants

4 Development
of larvae
in stems.
Deformation
of stems

4.1 Detail:
inside stem

Spring

Summer

> 12 °C first approach
to rape crops

Winter

Autumn

5 Larvae migrate
into the soil
and pupate

1 Beetles leave
the soil

6 Diapause

Occurrence and Importance

The rape stem weevil is common in Europe in areas where rape is cultivated. Regular damage occurs every year especially in France, southern Germany and in Austria. Severely injured plants are subject to yield losses of up to 50%. *C. napi* does not occur in Britain, but other related species occur and can cause similar damage.

Threshold

Ten weevils per yellow dish caught within three days during the period up to flowering.

Natural Enemies

Some species of ichneumon flies are parasites of the larvae of rape stem weevil.

Literature
Berger, H.-K., 1988: Die Bekämpfung des Rapsstengelrüßlers: Kein leicht zu lösendes Problem. Raps 6. Jg. (2), 86-87.
Hossfeld, R., 1987: Schadensschwellen bei tierischen Rapsschädlingen. Raps, 5. Jg. (2), 70-72.
Thioulouse, J., 1984: Lecharançon de la tige du chou *(Ceutorrhynchus napi* Gyll.). Informations Techniques CETIOM, 86.

Cabbage Stem Weevil *Ceutorhynchus quadridens Panz.*

Organism and Symptoms

The dull grey or rust - brown 2.5 - 3.5 mm long weevil, which in certain regions is also known as cabbage seedstalk curculio, is irregularly covered with greyish - white hairs which give the whole insect a mottled appearance. The thin proboscis is curved downward and the tips of the legs have a red dish coloura-

tion **❶**, **❷**. The creamy white arcuate larva has a yellow - brown head capsule and is 4 - 5 mm long.

There are no external malformations on attacked oilseed rape plants so that damage caused by the cabbage stem weevil is easy to distinguish from that caused by rape stem weevil **❹**, **❺**. The first visible symptoms are the punctures caused by the females during oviposition. Longitudinal sections of the stem near to the punctures show the tunnels

❻ dug by the larvae which re semble closely those of the rap stem weevil. The first two larva stages can be distinguished b the colour of the head capsul for the third larval instars, whos heads are identical in colour, it necessary to measure the widt of the head. The exit holes sitv ated at the stem base favour sec ondary infection by *Phoma li*

Synonym: C. pallidactylus Marsh.

...um and *Verticillium dahliae*, ...e agents of stem canker and ...ilt. Severe attacks can cause a ...duction in crop growth, and ...dging.

Biology

The life cycle of the cabbage stem weevil is similar to that of the rape stem weevil. The adults begin to fly at the same time as, or some days later than, the rape stem weevil. After a period of maturation feeding the females lay their eggs in the petioles or directly into the stem ❸. The larvae cause damage to the mid-ribs of the leaves, the petioles and later the stems. Later they leave the rape plants and, after a short pupal diapause ❼ in the soil, the adults emerge and begin their maturation feeding which usually coincides with the time of full crop maturity and is not injurious. Autumn and winter are passed by the adults in natural shelter.

④

⑤

Host Range

The cabbage stem weevil also attacks cabbage, turnip, swedes, radish, wild radish and other species of wild crucifers.

Occurrence and Importance

The cabbage stem weevil is recorded wherever rape is cultivated. The species can damage spring rape, but is much less injurious to winter rape than the rape stem weevil because there are no malformations of the stems. Even in the case of severe attacks yield losses are usually less than 20 %.

Threshold

The common threshold in Continental Europe for both species of stem weevils, *C. napi* and *C. quadridens*, is ten weevils per yellow dish in three days.

Literature
Winfield, A. L., 1961: Observation on the biology and control of the cabbage stem weevil, *Ceutorhynchus quadridens Panz.*, on Trowse Mustard (*Brassica juncea*). Bulletin of Entomological Research **52**, 589–600.

Rape Winter Stem Weevil *Ceutorhynchus picitarsis Gyll.*

Organism and Symptoms

The rape winter stem weevil is 2.4 - 3.7 mm long, metallic black, with a light scaly underside and reddish - brown tips to the legs ❶. The white, legless larvae are 4 - 5 mm long with a brown head capsule which later becomes yellow in colour ❸.

Adult weevils do little damage. The larvae tunnel in petioles and in the pith at the base of the stem or in the root collar and destroy the terminal shoot ❹. Longitudinal sections of the stem base will reveal the larvae which can sometimes destroy the whole plant during winter. However, in spring, often the first signs on less severely attacked plants are stunting and the production of many lateral shoots at the beginning of stem extension. The periods of flowering and maturation are prolonged on attacked plants and their growth habit is characterised by the proliferation of numerous lateral stems.

Biology

The adults migrate to oilseed rape fields (1) in late September and October and, about four weeks later, the females begin their oviposition (2) which may continue during the whole winter if the temperatures are not too low. The eggs are laid singly or in batches on the upper part of the petiole, near its point of insertion on the stem ❷. During winter, the larvae tunnel into the stem and the crown and feed there until spring (3, 3.1). The main shoot or the whole plant may be killed and overwinter losses and proliferation of lateral stems (4) are common. The mature larvae leave the plants (5) during April to pupate in the soil (6). The larvae can be distinguished from larvae of cabbage stem flea beetles, which are also found at the base of the stem, by the darker head and the absence of legs. The adults hatch in May and June and migrate to new rape crops in autumn after a summer passed in diapause (7).

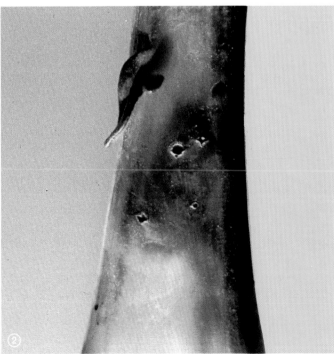

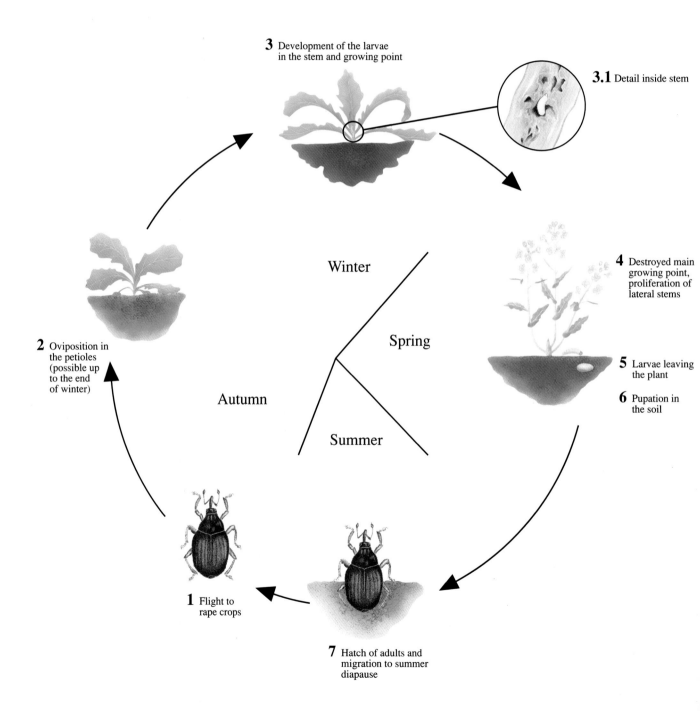

3 Development of the larvae
in the stem and growing point

3.1 Detail inside stem

4 Destroyed main
growing point,
proliferation of
lateral stems

Winter

Spring

5 Larvae leaving
the plant

6 Pupation in
the soil

2 Oviposition in
the petioles
(possible up
to the end
of winter)

Autumn

Summer

1 Flight to
rape crops

7 Hatch of adults and
migration to summer
diapause

Host Range

Rape winter stem weevils attack many species of crucifer, but prefer oilseed rape.

Occurrence and Importance

In Germany, after an interval of thirty years, rape winter stem weevil has recently been detected in some rape crops in the region around Munich. Swiss studies report economically important losses caused by this pest. In France it is common on oilseed rape in the regions north of the Loire river. In Britain, prior to 1982, it was uncommon, but has since increased locally in Lincolnshire and East Anglia to become a potentially serious pest.

Threshold

None established.

Natural Enemies

Various species of Hymenoptera are natural enemies of rape winter stem weevil larvae.

Literature

Büchi, R. ,1986: Biologie und Bekämpfung des Schwarzen Triebrüßlers, *Ceutorhynchus picitarsis* Gyll. (Col., Curculionidae). Anz. Schädlingskde, Pflanzenschutz, Umweltschutz **59**, 51–56.

Büchi, R. und Ridly, P., 1984: Bekämpfung des Schwarzen Triebrüßlers. - Raps, 2. Jg. (4),166-167.

Dosse, G., 1952: Zur Biologie und Morphologie des Schwarzen Triebrüßlers *Ceutorhynchus picitarsis* Gyll., mit differentialdiagnostischen Angaben zur Unterscheidung von *Ceutorhynchus napi* Gyll., C. *quadridens* Panz. und C. *picitarsis* Gyll – Z. Angew. Entomol. **34**, 303-312.

Jourdheuil, P., 1969: A propos du charancon noir d'hiver *(Ceutorhynchus picitarsis* Gyll.). – Bulletin Cetiom, **38**, 23-26.

Steck, U., 1985: Der Schwarze Triebrüßler. Bisher nur im Umkreis München. – Pflanzenschutz-Praxis, (2), 30-31.

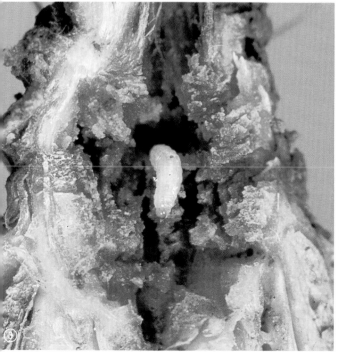

Cabbage Seed Weevil *Ceutorhynchus assimilis Payk.*

Organism and Symptoms

The cabbage seed weevil, also called cabbage seedpod weevil, is 2.5 - 3 mm long with black elytra covered by grey hairs thus appearing slate-grey overall. The head has the typical downward curved proboscis of weevils and the feet are black ❶. The 4 - 5 mm long, legless, white to yellow coloured larvae are slightly arcuate and possess a yellowish brown head capsule ❹.

The first external symptoms on plants appear only when the larvae leave the attacked pods after feeding on seeds during maturation. The larvae cause little damage, usually feeding on three to five seeds in a pod ❸. The attacked pods remain closed until maturity, the only externally visible symptom being a small exit hole of about 1 mm in diameter ❺.

Biology

The weevils spend autumn and winter in the litter of hedges and woods (1). In spring, they leave this shelter and begin to fly to oilseed rape fields in the period before flowering when the air temperatures exceed 13 °C (2). The main migration coincides with the beginning of flowering. In the crop, on being even minimally disturbed on plants by wind or by man the weevils drop to the ground. After maturation feeding (3) the females lay mostly single eggs inside pods ❷ (4). For this purpose they bore a hole in the pod wall which is later cicatrised. Eight to nine days later the larvae begin to hatch and to feed on the maturing seeds damaging at most five per pod (5.1). After four week spent inside the pods the larvae leave the plant (6) and pupate in the soil at 5-10 cm depth (6.1). In August the young weevils hatch (7) and move to crop and wild crucifers for their maturation feeding. In the same month they migrate to their overwintering quarters where they remain until spring (8). The cabbage seed weevil has one generation each year.

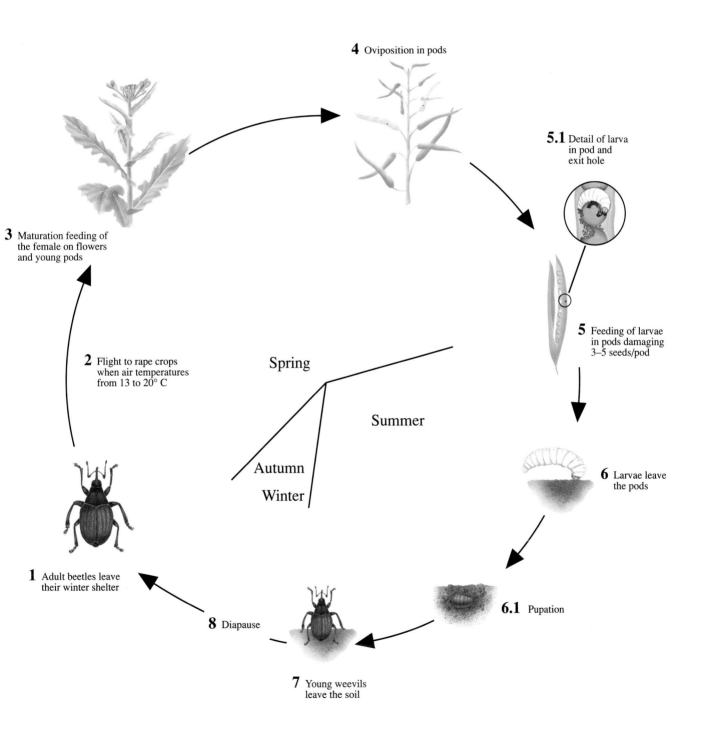

4 Oviposition in pods

5.1 Detail of larva in pod and exit hole

3 Maturation feeding of the female on flowers and young pods

5 Feeding of larvae in pods damaging 3–5 seeds/pod

2 Flight to rape crops when air temperatures from 13 to 20° C

Spring

Summer

Autumn

Winter

6 Larvae leave the pods

1 Adult beetles leave their winter shelter

6.1 Pupation

8 Diapause

7 Young weevils leave the soil

Host Range

Besides spring and winter oilseed rape the cabbage seed weevil attacks cabbage, radish, turnip, swede rape and various species of wild cruciferae especially those producing large pods.

Occurrence and Importance

The cabbage seed weevil is common in areas where oilseed rape is cultivated. The feeding and egg-laying punctures made by adults in young pods do no direct damage but provide suitable sites for brassica pod midges *(Dasineura brassicae)* to lay their eggs. Direct damage by weevil larvae is usually negligible, but secondary damage caused by the brassica pod midge may be significant. In addition, the penetration of water and pathogenic fungi into the pods is made easier and can cause premature germination and rotting of seed.

Threshold

- Before the stage flowering (winter rape): some weevils present on each of many plants.
- During flowering, with low risk of pod midge attacks: 1 weevils per plant
- During flowering, with high risk of pod midge attacks: 1 weevils per two plants.

Natural Enemies

The larvae of cabbage seed weevils are parasitised by the chalcid wasp *Trichomalus perfectus.*

Literature

Bonnemaison, L., 1957: Le charançon d siliques, biologie et méthodes de lutte. Ann. Epiphyties, **4**, 347–543.

Fröhlich, G., 1956: Zur Frage der biolo gischen Abhängigkeit der Kohlschoter Gallmücke *(Dasyneura brassicae* Winn. vom Kohlschotenrüßler *(Ceutorhynchu assimilis* Payk.).–Beitr. Entomol. **6**, 100 110.

Hoßfeld, R., 1987: Schadensschwelle bei tierischen Rapsschädlingen. Raps, (2), 70-72.

Lacote, J. P., 1974: Perspectives de lutt intégrée contre *Ceutorhynchus assimil* Payk. dans les cultures de colza d'hiver. Informations Techniques CETIOM, **38** 1–5.

Lerin, J., 1982: Estimation de l'action d charançon des siliques *(Ceuthorrhynchu assimilis)* sur la productivité du colz d'hiver. 1. Aspects méthodologiques.– Agronomie, **2** (10), 1005–1014.

Pollen (Blossom) Beetle *Meligethes aeneus F.*

Organism and Symptoms

The adult pollen beetle is 1.5 - 2.5 mm long, oval shaped and metallic greenish or bluish black (1). The creamy white, 3 . 5 - 4.0 mm long, larvae have a distinct, black - brown head and three pairs of short, dark brown legs. Their body segments are covered with sparse bristles and two or three dark spots on the upper side.

Adult feeding holes of different size can be found over the whole raceme of flower buds. The smaller buds may be completely destroyed while the larger ones show the holes made by beetles chewing into buds in search of pollen for food. The damaged buds shrink, wilt and later abort leaving the pedicels only ('blind stalks'), giving the whole raceme an irregular appearance ❹. If injury is very slight the buds may be able to produce pods which are malformed or twisted but never with swellings or galls.

Biology

The pollen beetles leave their winter quarters as soon as soil temperatures reach 10 °C (2). When air temperatures are higher than 15 °C they fly to nearby rape crops initially infesting the borders of the fields. With sunny and warm weather the whole field can soon be infested. The beetles feed almost exclusively on pollen (3). If attacks occur at early stages of bud formation this results in damage to sepals, petals, ovaries and the destruction of embryos (4). If flowering has begun the feeding habits of the beetle will not cause damage to the crop. The females lay their eggs, in groups of up to five, in the largest buds after biting a hole at the base of the bud ❷. The larvae hatch a few days later and feed on pollen and nectar like the adults ❸, but without injuring the ovaries. After three to four weeks mature the larvae leave the flowers (5) and pupate in the soil (6). The young beetles appear about two weeks later, usually in June or July, and begin maturation feeding on various crops and wild plants. At the end of August the beetles migrate to their winter quarters to hibernate in the litter of woods, hedges and embankments (1). There is a single generation per year.

①

Host Range

Many other cruciferous crops are attacked such as radish, brown and white mustard, seed crops of cabbage, turnip and swede. Adult beetles feed on a very wide range of wild crucifer species and many other pollen producing non - cruciferous plants are attacked although they do not breed on the latter.

Occurrence and Importance

Pollen beetles are abundant and widespread pests of oilseed rape, but are generally of little importance in winter rape unless the crop is backward or the insects appear during the early stages of bud formation or in years in which these stages persist for a long time. Damage is more serious on spring rape which is less able to compensate for early damage and loss of pods.

Threshold

Threshold numbers normally relate to the susceptible green to yellow bud stage. Opinions in Europe vary, from 3/plant in Poland to more than 15 - 20/plant in Britain; In Germany the numbers are much lower:
1) Winter oilseed rape;
– at a very early stage (buds still covered):
   1- 2 beetles / plant
– at an early stage (two weeks before flowering):
   4 beetles / plant
– late (shortly before flowering):
   5 - 6 beetles / plant

2) Spring oilseed rape;
   2 beetles / plant.

These spray thresholds are guidelines only, and at the green to yellow bud stage in winter rape they should be at least doubled for lush, dense, well fertilised crops.

Natural Enemies

Different species of coccinellid beetles and ichneumon flies are predators or parasites of pollen beetles.

Literature

AID, 1985: Integrierter Pflanzenschutz **32**, 30–31.

Fritzsche, R., 1957: Zur Biologie und Ökologie der Rapsschädlinge der Gattung **Meligethes**. Z. angew. Entomologie **40**, 222–280.

Gould, H. J., 1975: Surveys of pest incidence on oilseed rape in south central England. Annals of Applied Biology **7** (1), 19–26.

Hoßfeld, R., 1987: Schadensschwellen bei tierischen Rapsschädlingen, Raps (2), 70–72

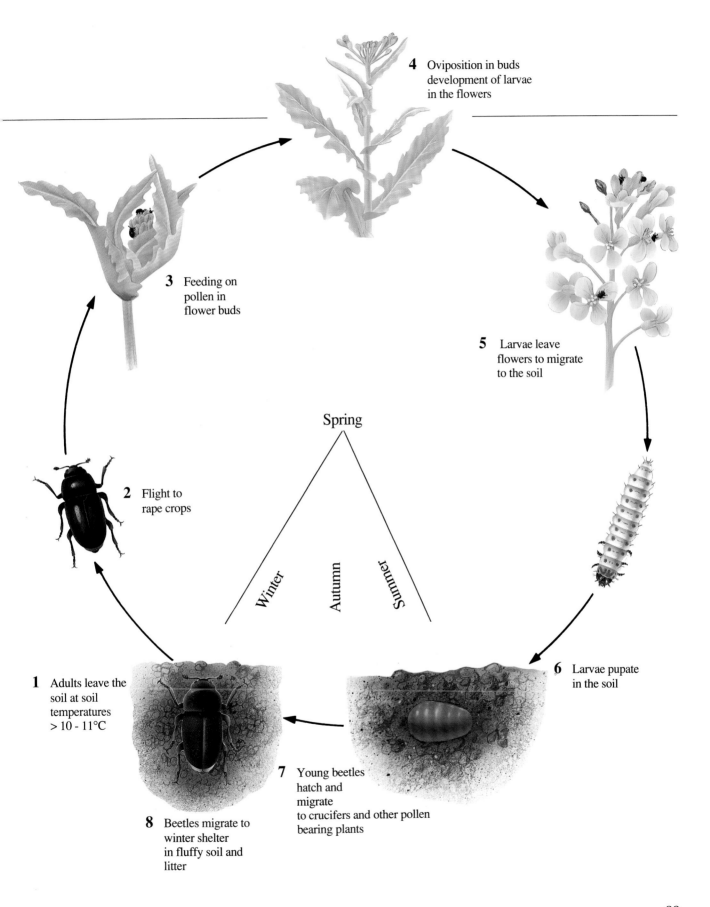

4 Oviposition in buds development of larvae in the flowers

3 Feeding on pollen in flower buds

5 Larvae leave flowers to migrate to the soil

Spring

2 Flight to rape crops

Winter

Autumn

Summer

6 Larvae pupate in the soil

1 Adults leave the soil at soil temperatures > 10 - 11°C

7 Young beetles hatch and migrate to crucifers and other pollen bearing plants

8 Beetles migrate to winter shelter in fluffy soil and litter

Flies and Midges

Cabbage Root Fly *Delia (Synonyms: Hylemyia, Phorbia etc.) radicum L.*

Organism and Symptoms

There are several species of flies *(Delia* spp.)on brassicas, the most common of them on rape being the small cabbage root fly ❶. The 5 - 6 mm long adult resembles the common house fly but has red eyes on its silverwhite head. The male is greyish black and the female greyish brown in colour. The legless larvae (maggots) are 7 - 8 mm long. The brown, 4 - 7 mm long puparium is barrel - shaped.

The root collar and roots, especially of younger plants, are covered with brown discolourations and rotten flecks. Parts of the lateral roots may die and are lost when the plant is pulled from the soil. The larvae feed usually in the outer layers of the attacked parts leaving numerous tunnels and necrotic tissues ❷ causing wilting. Sometimes they live in the feeding tunnels left by other insects such as cabbage stem flea beetles *(P. chrysocephala)* and several species of weevils *(Ceutorhynchus* spp.) and increase the damage caused by the latter. Severely injured plants are stunted or may be killed.

Biology

After overwintering as a pupa the adult flies hatch in the month of April or May and leave the soil. About a week later the females lay their 1 mm long, white eggs in batches of about one hundred directly onto the root collar or into cracks in the soil. The larvae hatch four to eight days later feeding at first on small lateral roots and later on the main root. After three to four weeks the larvae usually pupate in the soil but sometimes also in the attacked tissues. A second generation appears in July or August and a third one in September or October. The latter generation may infest newly sown oilseed rape crops. The life span of the adult is about eight to fifteen days.

Host Range

The cabbage root fly lives on cabbage, rape, broccoli, turnip rape and stubble turnips and on wild crucifers such as wild mustard and radish and on field penny-cress.

Occurrence and Importance

The economic importance of root fly attacks on rape crops is not yet well studied. The first generation can be injurious to the crop especially in seasons with dry weather during the months of May and June. Severe autumnal attack, in which more than half of the root surface of the plants may be destroyed, increases the likelihood that plants will be killed by frost in winter.

Threshold

None established.

Natural Enemies

There are many known natural enemies of the cabbage root fly. The most important predators of eggs are the carabid beetles.

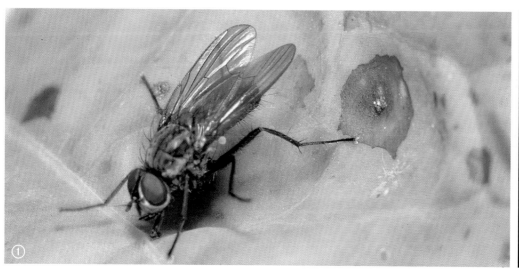

Cabbage Leaf Miner *Phytomyza rufipes Meig.*

Organism and Symptoms

The cabbage leaf miner, also called cabbage leaf stalk blister fly is grey and up to 3 mm long. The legless larva reaches a length of 6 mm and has no distinct head although the internal mouth-hooks at the head end are visible. A blotch miner *(Scaptomyza flava)* can also occur on rape leaves.

The feeding tunnels of cabbage leaf miner can be seen in the petioles and on the upper leaf surface, running firstly parallel to the leaf veins ❶, ❷ and later in larger areas. Sometimes larvae penetrate directly into veins so that little or no damage is seen on the lamina. The larvae feed inside the tunnels and are often associated with those of stem flea beetles *(P. chrysocephala)*. Affected leaves often yellow or wilt and may drop off prematurely. Leaf miner larvae are never injurious to the shoot tip.

Biology

The adults hatch at the end of April or in early May. The number of generations completed in a year varies from one to three depending on climate and season. Before winter the larvae pupate in the soil.

Occurrence and Importance

The cabbage leaf miner is wide spread but unimportant and confined to crucifers, mainly brassicas. Rape is usually attacked in autumn and, the stem not being affected, damage is never serious; crops tolerate any premature loss of leaves. Chemical control has not been necessary to date.

Treshold

Not known.

Brassica Pod Midge *Dasineura brassicae Winn.*

Organism and Symptoms

The brassica pod midge or bladder pod midge is very small and delicate, 1.2 -1.5 mm long, black - brown in colour with white hairs on the upper thorax and long legs. The reddish abdomen has brown lateral bands and the head has two long antennae ❶, ❷. The legless larvae are 0.5 -1.5 mm long with no head and are initially transparent and then white or yellowish in colour ❸.

Single pods on the main raceme and later on the lateral branches become yellow and swollen with larvae feeding inside ❹. The stunted, curved or shrivelled pods split prematurely and shed seeds ❺.

Biology

The adults emerge in spring from pupae in cocoons near the soil surface in fields which have grown brassicas the preceding season. The midges are poor fliers and can only reach crops situated near their overwinter sites. The main flying period begins when the first flowers are seen in the crop. The adult females live for three or four days only and lay their eggs in groups of up to sixty in pods using the bore holes left by other insects, especially those of the cabbage seed weevil *(C. assimilis)*. Such damage is normally required for oviposition by the midge, but it can also occur in very young, up to 1 cm long, thin walled, or otherwise damaged, pods. The larvae feed on the inner walls of the pods and on the seeds and excrete toxic compounds which cause swelling, premature yellowing and shattering of the pods. Later the larvae migrate to the soil and pupate in an earthen cocoon. The adults of the second generation hatch usually during the time of flowering of summer crucifers. The cocoons produced by the second generation may remain dormant until spring or hatch in the same year giving a third generation.

Host Range

The brassica pod midge lives mainly on rape, brown and white mustard, seed crops of turnip rape, swede, garden turnip, radish and on wild crucifers.

Occurrence and Importance

It is a widespread and common pest in areas where oilseed rape is grown, but damage is rarely economically important except where there are many cabbage seed weevils predisposing the pods to oviposition by the midges. Often only the first generation is injurious and damage is confined to the headlands.

Threshold

Specific control for pod midge is not usually warranted; control of cabbage seed weevil will normally also control the midge. However, in Germany the following thresholds are used:

Visual counts:
– where there is little damage by seed weevils,
  1 midge / plant
– where there is much damage by seed weevils,
  1 midge /3 - 4 plants

Sweepnet counts:
– 2 midges /10 sweepnet strokes.

Natural Enemies

Among the numerous parasites of the brassica pod midge are *Platygaster oebalus* Walk. and *Aphanogmus abdominalis* Thoms.

Literature

Buhl, C., 1959: Beitrag zur Frage der biologischen Abhängigkeit der Kohlschotenmücke *(Dasyneura brassica* Winn.) von dem Kohlschotenrüßler *(Ceutorhynchus assimilis* Payk.). Z. Pflanzenkr. Pflanzenschutz **64**, 562-568.

Coutin, R., 1961: La cécidomyie du colza. Phytoma, **131**.

Coutin, R., 1964: Le comportement de ponte chez plusieurs cécidomyies en relation avec l'état de développement chez la plante hôte des organes recherchés pour l'oviposition Rev.-Zool Agricole **4**.

Fröhlich, G., 1956: Zur Biologie und Bekämpfung der Kohlschoten-Gallmücke *(Dasyneura brassicae* Winn.). Nachrichtenbl. Dtsch. Pflanzenschutzdienst (Berl.) NF **10**,123–128.

Doberitz, G., 1971: Untersuchungen über die biologische Abhängigkeit der Kohlschotenmücke *(Dasyneura brassicae* Winn.) vom Kohlschotenrüßler *(Ceutorhynchus assimilis* Payk.) und Vorschläge zur Verbesserung ihrer Bekämpfung. – Diss. Halle.

Sawflies

Turnip Sawfly *Athalia rosae L. (Synonym: A. colibri Christ.)*

Organism and Symptoms

The turnip sawfly, also called swede sawfly, is 6 - 8 mm long with a shiny black head and thorax and yellow to orange abdomen without a constriction between abdomen and thorax ❶. The yellowish wings are transparent and membranous with a dark anterior margin. The larvae or caterpillars are up to 18 mm long, initially light grey to light green ❷ and later dark green to velvet black ❸ with three pairs of thoracic, seven pairs of abdominal and one pair of additional (anal) legs. The lateral and ventral surfaces of the larvae are grey.

The first larval stages feed on young rape plants causing complete perforations and also symptoms of 'window feeding'. The older larvae bite off the margins of the leaves sometimes leaving only the main veins ❹.

Biology

The last larval stage of the turnip sawfly overwinters in a silken cocoon and only changes into a pupa in spring. The adults hatch in May or June. The female cuts the leaf margins with a sawlike ovipositor and lays single eggs into the pockets produced in this way. Each female lays a total of 50 to 300 eggs. After six to ten days the larvae hatch and begin feeding. After three moults the larvae pupate in the soil at a depth of 1- 5 cm. In July or August, a second generation of the insect feeds on catch crop rape or on mustard. A third generation may appear, depending on the local climate, which feeds on young oilseed rape plants.

Host Range

Many crops are possibl hosts for the turnip sawfly oilseed rape, brown and whit mustard, stubble turnips an radish. Wild crucifers are als attacked.

①

94

Occurrence and Importance

Oilseed rape is rarely damaged and effects on yield are negligible. The pest is rare in Britain. However, in Continental Europe, rape and mustard grown as catch crops for fodder or green manuring are often invaded by sawfly larvae which cause severe damage especially if the weather in autumn is warm and dry.

Threshold

The threshold level in Germany is 1- 2 larvae / plant.

Natural Enemies

Populations of turnip sawfly are controlled by various flies and nematodes parasitic on the larvae.

Literature

Ohnesorge, B., 1977: Beobachtungen zur Biologie der Rübsenblattwespe, Athalia rosae L. *(Hym. tenthredinidae)*. Anz. Schädlingskd. Pflanzenschutz Umweltschutz **52**, 70–73

Reich, R. , 1961: Beiträge zur Biologie der Rübsenblattwespe (*Athalia rosae* L.). Nachrichtenbl. Dtsch. Pflanzenschutzdienst (Berl.) NF **15**, 161–175.

Aphids

Cabbage Aphid *Brevicoryne brassicae L.*

Organism and Symptoms

The 2.2 mm long wingless aphids are mealy grey in appearance, as if dusted with powder ❶. On their backs they have two rows of dark spots. The 2.5 mm long winged stages have a black head, dark thorax and a yellowish or green abdomen with black spots.

Bluish grey, mealy colonies of the aphids cover stems and terminal racemes. Heavy infestations may be obvious on individual plants, particularly on crop headlands ❶, ❷. As a consequence of sucking damage the parts of the plant situated above the colonies turn yellow and die ❸. Red discolouration, twisting, curling and malformation of the attacked parts also occurs ❹. In favourable conditions the aphids spread rapidly over the whole plant and to neighbouring plants.

If the season is very favourable there may be infestation early in autumn ❻ producing leaf clearing ❺ and curling ❼

Biology

Overwintering of the mealy cabbage aphid is usually by eggs, but sometimes also by the wingless adults and always on crucifers. The eggs are black and 0.5 mm long. Reproduction begins in spring so that colonies of wingless and, at the end of spring, winged adults can be found. The latter are able to fly to other oilseed rape fields or to horticultural brassicas (cabbages). Up to ten generations of winged and wingless adults are produced in summer with the latest generations feeding on newly sown rape. Fecund females begin oviposition on crucifers in autumn.

Host Range

The host range includes cauliflower, Brussels sprouts, swedes, cabbage, turnip, mustard, radish and many wild species of crucifers such as charlock and shepherd's purse.

Occurrence and Importance

The mealy cabbage aphid is a common pest on rape, but severe attacks are usually limited to headlands or to isolated plants and to certain years. Rarely, in years favouring widespread infestation, some yield loss may occur.

Threshold

None established.

Natural Enemies

Many species of predators are natural enemies of the cabbage aphid. The most important ones are larvae of coccinellid beetles and of syrphid flies.

Literature

Messelière de la, C., 1983: *Brevicoryne brassicae:* nuisibilité. Prévisions des attaques sur colza d' hiver et techniques de lutte. – 6ème Congrès International sur le Colza, Paris.

Daebeler, F. und Hinz, B., 1980: Schadwirkung der Mehligen Kohlblattlaus *(Brevicoryne brassicae L.)* bei Herbst- und Frühjahrsbefall an Winterraps. Nachrichtenbl, Pflanzenschutz DDR **34**, 16-17.

Several species of nematode, or eelworm, can parasitise oilseed rape although economic damage is not often encountered. However, rape and other cultivated brassicas may serve as intermediate hosts and permit the reproduction of nematodes which are injurious to other crops. Yield losses caused by the beet cyst nematode on sugar beet are increased in rotations with brassicas. In addition, the lesions produced by nematodes on oilseed rape tend to favour secondary attack by pathogenic fungi.

Brassica Cyst Nematode

Heterodera cruciferae Franklin

Severe attacks on rape and other cultivated crucifers produce patches of stunted plants in the field. Infested roots carry small, 0.5 mm long, lemon - shaped cysts of females containing the eggs.

Beet Cyst Nematode

Heterodera schachtii Schmidt

The beet cyst nematode is not reported to be harmful to rape crops but it may reproduce on them and on other cultivated and weed crucifers. Lemon - shaped cysts of females, 0,5 mm long, occur on the roots so increasing nematode numbers and thus increasing yield losses in subsequent sugar beet crops on the same field.

Root Lesion Nematode

Pratylenchus neglectus Rensch

Different species of root lesion nematodes, also called migratory nematodes, particularly species of the genus *Pratylenchus*, produce stunting on rape without formation of cysts on roots. The nematodes enter the root cortex and live there as intercellular parasites causing necrosis of the cortical cells and forming cavities in the root which later may be invaded by secondary fungi and bacteria. Swedish studies demonstrated that attacks of *Verticillium dahliae* were favoured by previous attacks of *Pratylenchus penetrans*.

Stem Eelworm

Ditylenchus dipsaci Kühn

Severe attacks by stem eelworm, also called stem and bulb nematode, cause twisted and thickened leaves on young rape plants. The parasite completes several generations in the attacked tissues and returns to the soil with the remains of the vegetation where it can remain viable for several years.

Birds

Woodpigeon *Columba palumbus L.*

Damage caused by birds is very common on oilseed rape. From late autumn until spring pigeons may cause considerable loss of foliage

Cause and Symptoms

The adult woodpigeon has slate grey plumage, darker on the wings and black on the tail, with irridescent green or purple feathers and characteristic white patches on the collar and a white bar on each wing. The white patches are absent in young birds.

In autumn, winter and spring woodpigeons often appear in huge flocks causing severe damage on oilseed rape ❶, ❷, peas, cabbages and on cruciferous catch crops. The leaves are grazed leaving only the main veins ❸. Frequently the growing point is severely damaged causing the production later of new lateral shoots at the stem base. The reduction in crop vigour, delayed development and patchiness, can cause problems at harvest.

Sparrows and Finches *Passer spp., Carduelis spp.*

Cause and Symptoms

Some species of small birds, such as house sparrows *(Passer domesticus)* and tree sparrows *(Passer montanus)* and some finches like the greenfinch *(Carduelis chloris)* and the linnet *(Carduelis cannabina)*, pick the seeds out of the pods of oilseed rape causing localized damage or premature shattering **❶**, **❷**.

The tree sparrow is slightly smaller than the house sparrow and is distinguishable by the black flecks on its white cheeks. Both species are plurivorous and cause damage on oilseed rape in the period immediately before harvest. Crops affected by flocks of sparrows are easily recognized by the presence of shattered and partially or totally empty pods. The house sparrow occurs much more frequently and causes damage in fields situated on the urban fringe and in the neighbourhood of buildings or villages.

Mammals

At certain sites rape may be severely damaged by mammals, especially rodents; wild rabbits, hares, black water rats and sometimes also common voles may cause serious damage. Other mammals which cause considerable losses are roe deer, red deer and fallow deer which graze in oilseed rape crops. If the leaves only are grazed, the plants are likely to recover, but if the growing points are lost the possibility of producing lateral shoots is precluded.

Wild Rabbit

Oryctolagus cuniculus L.

Cause and Symptoms

The 35 - 48 cm long wild rabbit has short (about 7 cm long) ears without black tips and a white tail. The dorsal fur is brown, yellowish - grey or yellowish - brown in colour.

All aerial parts of young oilseed rape plants may be partially or wholly grazed while on older plants only the leaves are eaten.

Occurrence and Importance

Damage can be regular in certain places and years and especially serious on field margins near burrows.

Hare

Lepus europaeus (L.) Pall.

Cause and Symptoms

Hares are much larger, up to about 68 cm long, with tawny brown fur and black tips on their long ears and tail.

Their feeding habits are similar to those of rabbits.

Occurrence and Importance

In contrast with rabbits, hares are solitary, never occuring in high population densities, and they do not cause important losses on rape crops.

Black Water Rat

Arvicola terrestris L.

Cause and Symptoms

Black water rats, sometimes also called voles, are 12 - 16 cm long rodents with a long tail half the length of the body.

Damage is caused by the feeding habits of the species which bites off the roots and produces mounds of disturbed soil so giving infested crops an uneven appearance.

Occurrence and Importance

In Continental Europe black water rats can be occasionally injurious to oilseed rape and also to pastures, horticultural crops, forage grasses and orchards.

Common Vole

Microtus arvalis Pall.

Cause and Symptoms

The common vole, also called 'field mouse', is 9 - 11 cm and sometimes even 15 cm long and has a tail one third the length of the body.

In contrast with the black water rat, the field mouse feeds on the aerial parts of plants as well as on roots.

Occurrence and Importance

In Europe the field mouse is occasionally injurious to oilseed rape, to cereals, sugar beet, potatoes, forage grasses and to many other crops.

Honey Bee *Apis mellifera L.*

There are many species of beneficial insects in oilseed rape crops, e.g. the numerous species of natural enemies mentioned in the chapters dealing with each pest.

Oilseed rape, being self fertile, does not depend on bees or similar insects to produce seeds although pod setting may be enhanced by the activity of bees during flowering. Rape is a good source of nectar and has become of considerable importance to beekeepers **②** as the crop area has increased in recent years. Many ingredients in formulations used for pest control in oilseed rape are toxic to honey bees **①** and this fact should be taken into account in the planning of control measures.

Some **basic rules**:
- Carry out treatments in flowering crops only if absolutely necessary.
- Apply pesticides in flowering crops only in the evening when bee flights have ceased. Use exclusively formulations which are declared to be harmless to bees when treating fields with open flowers on the crop or on weeds.

- Some formulations declared as 'harmful to bees' must not be sprayed before the end of the daily flight of bees. Spraying should cease before 11.00 p.m. to allow the deposit to dry off before the next morning.
- Do not apply formulations which are harmful to bees within 60 m of beehives without first informing the beekeeper.

Pest Detection and Targeted Control

Yellow Dish Trap

The necessity for targeted pest and disease control in oilseed rape, rather than indiscriminate use of pesticides, should be self evident. The principles of integrated control also ought to be respected and known thresholds for spray applications taken into account. For certain pests of oilseed rape the critical densities are known and economical use of insecticides is possible. The economic spray threshold is attained if the monetary benefits of a certain treatment exceed its costs.

The use of spray thresholds presupposes knowledge about the pest population densities, the damage that may follow, and suitable methods of control for each pest.

Yellow dish trap

Yellow dish traps are widely used to detect the first approaches and flying activity of injurious insects, especially weevils and beetles ❶, ❷. The following points should be considered for their construction and appropriate use:

- **Materials:** round or rectangular dishes, or containers which have been cut open, of a yellow colour similar to rape flowers; 2 m long metal poles with a device for holding the dishes.
- **Filling:** the traps are half filled with water containing a few drops of detergent to reduce surface tension and so prevent insects escaping. Small holes should be made about 5 cm beneath the rim of the dish to avoid overflow caused by rain.
- **Position:** the yellow dishes are set up about 20 m from the border of the field and at a height above ground deter-

mined by the growth of the crop ❷. On larger areas there should be a yellow dish on each side of the field.
- **Examination:** The dishes should be examined at regular intervals and preferably near mid - day.
- **High captures** can be expected in warm and sunny weather, low captures in cold or rainy weather.
- **Information** on population densities (number of insects plant or number of insects unit area) must be ascertained by additional surveys e.g. by shaking 5 x 10 racemes over a sheet of white paper or cloth

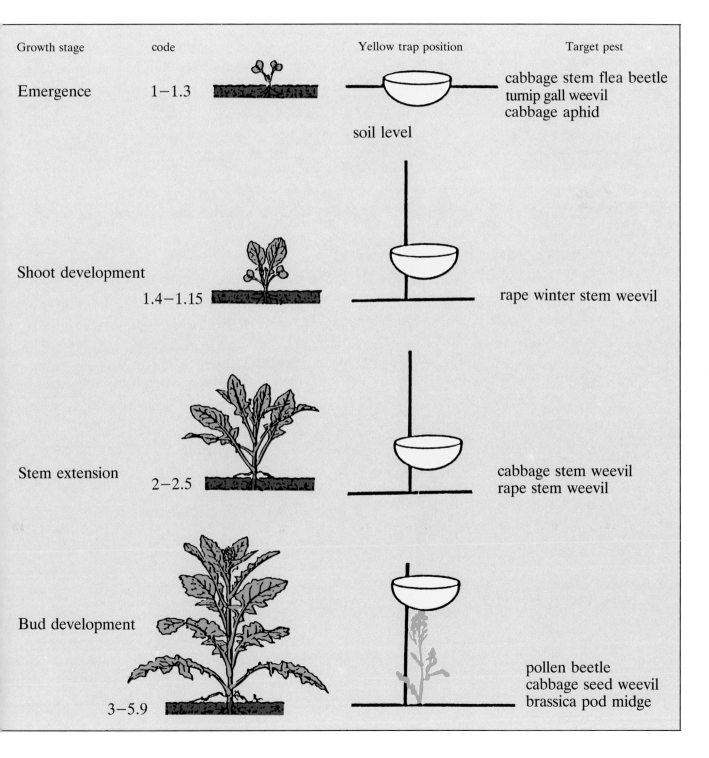

Growth stage	code	Yellow trap position	Target pest
Emergence	1−1.3	soil level	cabbage stem flea beetle turnip gall weevil cabbage aphid
Shoot development	1.4−1.15		rape winter stem weevil
Stem extension	2−2.5		cabbage stem weevil rape stem weevil
Bud development	3−5.9		pollen beetle cabbage seed weevil brassica pod midge

Nonparasitic
Diseases

Frost Damage

Frost Damage

Causes and Symptoms

Low temperatures are not the only cause of plant loss in winter. Poor development, plants not gradually acclimatised to low temperatures, extreme differences in temperatures and changing periods of frost and sunshine are the complex of conditions which can cause death over winter. In the absence of snow cover and with rapidly dropping temperatures there can be severe losses of plants ❶, ❷ particularly in poorly developed, late - sown crops or in overfertilised and extending early - sown crops ❸. The damage is increased on humid sites when a mild autumn is followed by a sudden frost of more than 15 °C below zero without snow cover. In spring the inverse phenomenon occurs, with late frosts damaging plants which have lost their winter hardiness.

At the end of winter patche of dead plants are seen in fields with the neighbouring plant showing yellow or reddish t brownish leaves which finall

rop off. The petioles and stems o not have tunnels such as ose created by larvae of flea eetles *(P. chrysocephala).*

Severely injured plants have their discoloured leaves lying flat on the soil, the shoot tip killed and the roots rotting ❷.

Frequently, only the leaves are injured with the older leaves bronzing at their tips and the younger ones covered with white to grey frost marks ❹. If the shoot tip is not injured these plants may recover with good husbandry and produce normal yields.

Sometimes plants are seen with nearly longitudinal fissures on the root collar with cicatrised margins. Plants damaged in this way later produce many leaves and lateral stems with poor pod setting.

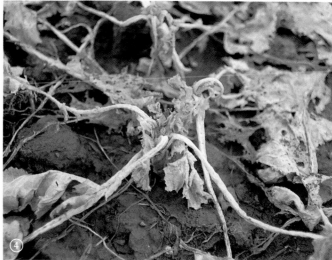

Late Frost Damage

Cause and Symptoms

Frost in late spring causes twisting of the stems ❷ which may straighten up again after a short time.

Sometimes water transport is hindered and the racemes become flaccid and hang down ❹. The tips appear to be wilting, but recovery is sometimes possible when frost has passed.

Frost during early flowering causes splits in the stems ❶, which, with humid weather may, ❷ undergo a soft rot. This damage is similar to the stem splitting caused by the rape stem weevil *(C. napi)*. On the other hand, stems attacked by weevil are more likely to split with late frosts.

①

②

Frost during full flowering causes curving of the plants ❸ which are sometimes also bent over completely.

Persistent cold weather or frost during the stages of flowering and pod formation result in reduced pod setting and shrivelled seeds.

Hail Injury

Hail Injury

Cause and Symptoms

The leaves hit by hailstones show whitish discolourations, cracks, holes and breakages. Sometimes the whole leaf is knocked off.

On stems injured by hail the epidermal cells are crushed and produce more or less widespread white - grey flecks and sometimes large wounds. At the beginning and especially at the end of flowering severely damaged stems bend over and may have open wounds. The affected main or lateral stem is often split to half its diameter, but the re-generative power of the plant often allows the stem to straighten up again. Severe damage with more than half of the diameter of the stem cut off results in complete loss of the stem ❶. Sometimes the whole main or lateral stem is cut off. Stems and leaves injured by hail showers tend to be attacked by fungi penetrating through the wounds (e.g. *P. lingam, B. cinerea*).

Buds, flowers and pods or parts of them may be knocked off or broken by hailstones ❷, ❸.

After the end of flowering the plant is not able to compensate with further growth for the dead or damaged parts and losses will be particularly severe or even total.

Hail showers on immature pods will not cause pod shattering but formation of small, stunted seeds at the point of impact ❷; oviposition of brassica pod midge *(D. brassicae)* may be favoured. Malformation and premature shattering of pods occurs and the damage may be enhanced by dark pod spot disease *(A. brassicae)*.

On mature crops near to harvest even slight hailshowers may cause pod shattering and seed losses ❹.

Occurrence and Importance

Oilseed rape is a crop which is particularly sensitive to hail injury. The growth stages from early ripening until harvest are most susceptible to damage. Unfortunately, the most severe hailstorms usually occur in this period. On crops which are ripe for harvesting even moderate hailstorms may cause complete yield loss.

Herbicide Damage

Causes and Symptoms

Residues of soil acting herbicides given to the preceding crop may cause difficulties for the emergence of oilseed rape ❶; malformed or stunted seedlings are frequently seen.

Herbicides recommended for use on oilseed rape can cause damage to the crop if they are overdosed, if the seeds germinate too fast, or if heavy rain immediately after sowing creates muddy soil conditions. Pale grey to brown areas of variable size can occur on the margins of the cotyledons and leaves ❸. If injury is severe the upper stem portions are damaged as well and young plants are killed or stunted ❷.

Spray drift of even minimal quantities of hormone-type herbicides applied to cereal crops can cause malformations of both aerial and underground plant parts of rape and result in severe damage. The affected

plants show enhanced but disarranged growth with malformation and curving of leaves and stems **4**, thickened shoots, hyperplastic tissues, production of numerous lateral stems, leaf discolourations, formation of tumours on the root collar and production of many lateral roots

5. The plants are killed or at least unable to set a normal number of flowers and pods, and the yield is reduced.

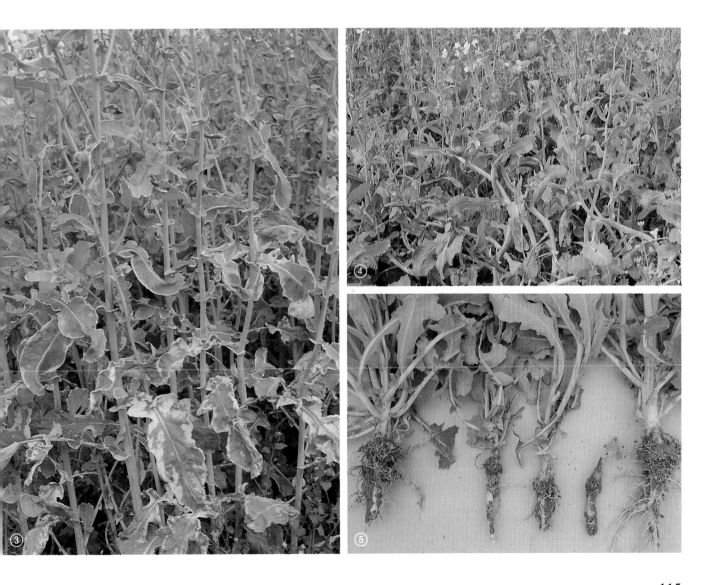

Drought Damage

Bud Wilting

Causes and Symptoms

The precise cause of bud wilting is not yet known. The disease is probably caused by changes in water and nutrient supply to which rape reacts very sensitively. The syndrome is seen in spring on winter and spring oilseed rape crops if long, cool, dry periods are followed by sunny, warm days.

The flowers in the middle and lower parts of the raceme remain in the bud stage, become dry and yellow - grey or white, wilt and drop off. The flowers in the upper parts of the raceme develop normally. At harvest, obviously shortened racemes can be attributed mistakenly to pollen beetle *(M. aeneus)* damage. The distinction is made possible by the complete loss of pods in the lower part of the raceme and by the absence of feeding damage on the remaining pods.

Growth Splits

Growth splits ❶ are frequently seen on the stems of rape if heavy rain occurs after a long period of dry weather with reduced plant growth rates. The splits usually cicatrise after a few days thus excluding attacks of parasitic organisms, but if spores of the agent of stem canker *(P. lingam)* arrive on the wounds there may be secondary infection.

Nitrogen Scorch

Cause and Symptoms

Large amounts of nitrogen fertiliser, especially when given a single application and in liquid form as urea or urea ammonium nitrate in autumn or spring, can sometime cause extensive chlorosis of leaves ❶. New growth in spring normally allows recovery from this damage.

Similar symptoms occur if large amounts of solid nitrogen, for example as prilled or granular urea or nitro-chalk or calcium ammonium nitrate (Nitrochalk), are applied during stem extension. Such damage often occurs if the fertiliser is applied after cool, humid weather is followed by dry conditions. Under these conditions, buds may be scorched and later turn brown and die ❷. This damage may occur too late for new growth to compensate for loss of buds.

Nutritional Disorders

Like other species of brassicas oilseed rape has a high requirement for the main nutritional elements nitrogen, phosphorus, potassium, sulphur, calcium and magnesium and for the trace elements boron, molybdenum, manganese, copper and zinc.

The general requirements are much times greater than those of cereals, the need for calcium is five times greater. The uptake of potassium, calcium and magnesium is considerably higher than the quantities left on the field by crop debris.

Acute or latent deficiencies of one or more elements can occur under certain soil conditions and cropping intensities. Plants affected by acute deficiencies are recognisable by visible symptoms while the much more common latent deficiencies are not visible and can be ascertained only by soil or plant analyses.

Frequently nutrient deficiencies are caused by a complex of factors.

Nitrogen Deficiency

Nitrogen is considered to be the engine of plant development and yield; it is the most important element in plant nutrition.

Symptoms

Insufficient supply of nitrogen causes translocation of the element from the older to the younger leaves. In spring there may be a visible yellowing of the lower leaves which later disappears when nitrogen supply is renewed by fertilizer application.

Potassium Deficiency

Symptoms

Potassium - or potash deficiencies occur mainly on light, acid and poorly drained soils. The symptoms are, besides wilting, dark green colouration and undulation of the leaves, especially under intense sunshine ❶, ❷. White to yellow - brown areas are seen first on the lower and then on the upper leaves proceeding from the leaf margins to the centre of the lamina ❷. If the deficiency persists the single areas coalesce, leaf margins become curled upward and the whole leaf dies.

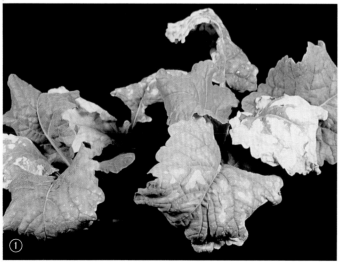

Magnesium Deficiency

Although the needs of oilseed rape for magnesium are high deficiencies are rarely seen.

Symptoms

Magnesium deficiency occurs frequently on crops growing in light and acid soil. Older leaves show interveinal clearing ❶ with the areas near to the main veins remaining green. Later the cleared zones become yellow, orange or red - brown in colour and necrotic ❷, the leaves appearing to be speckled. If the deficiency persists the symptoms spread and the whole leaf dies.

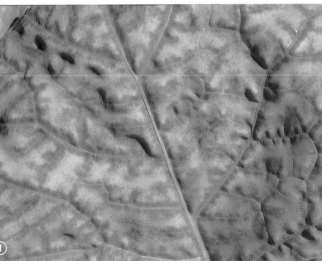

Calcium Deficiency

Although the needs of oilseed rape for calcium are high deficiencies are rarely seen.

Symptoms

Calcium deficient plants show damage at the ends of racemes ❶, similar in appearance to bud wilting caused by drought and to damage caused by attacks of grey mould *(B. cinerea)*.

Copper Deficiency

Copper deficiencies are very rarely seen on oilseed rape.

Symptoms

The leaves of oilseed rape plants affected by acute copper deficiency show interveinal clearings which later extend to the whole leaf and cause necrosis ❶.

Literature
Schnug, E., 1987: Spurennährstoffversorgung im intensiven Rapsanbau, Raps **5**, Jg. (1) 18–20

①

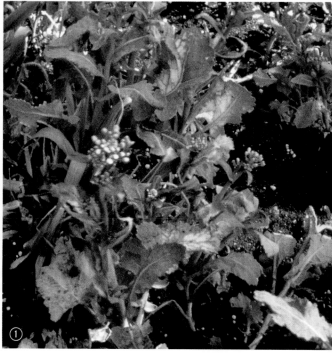

①

Manganese Deficiency

Manganese deficiencies are rarely seen on oilseed rape. If there is acute deficiency the plants can be cured with applications of foliar nutrients during stem extension.

Symptoms

Plants growing on calcareous or sandy soils with high pH values (6.5 - 8.0) tend to manifest symptoms of manganese deficiency.

The leaves inserted on the middle of the stem show ill - defined cloudy discolourations ❶ which later extend to the whole lamina and cause, in cases of severe deficiency, the death of the whole leaf and white to light brown discolourations.

Molybdenum Deficiency

Although the needs of rape, like those of all species of crucifers, for molybdenum are high, deficiencies are rarely seen.

Symptoms

Molybdenum deficiency occurs frequently on acid soil and is favoured by calcium deficiency.

Leaves show yellowish interveinal clearings and necroses. Another symptom of acute molybdenum deficiency is malformation of the leaves ❶, ranging from cup shaped curling of the margins to reduced development of the lamina.

Boron Deficiency

Boron has a special position among the trace elements because the needs of oilseed rape are about ten times greater than those of cereals, with deficiencies occurring frequently.

The necessity for boron fertilisation can be established by soil analysis before sowing. If applications of boron - phosphorus or of multiple combinations are necessary care should be taken to avoid an overdose which may damage succeeding crops of sensitive cereals, especially winter wheat. To avoid injury to rape the concentration of solutions for foliar application should be less than one per cent and the spray should be applied early in the morning or late in the afternoon.

Symptoms

Boron deficiency occur mainly in conditions where th element may be present but les available to plants, e.g. in alka line soils or after liming. Th deficiency is enhanced b drought.

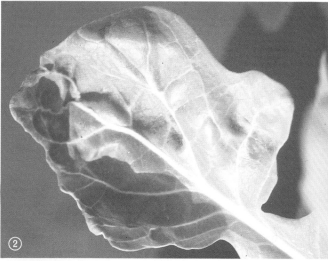

The younger leaves are curled ❶ and undulated, with their margins curved upward ❸ and frequently with the lamina ...d to yellow - brown in colour. ... the deficiency persists the ...aves are stunted ❸ and thick-ned ❷. The petioles and stems how scarred longitudinal fis-...res ❹. With early and ex-...eme deficiencies the shoot tip is necrosed and numerous lateral branches are produced. The number of pods and the number of seeds in each pod is decreased ❺.

Literature
Abercron, M. v., 1985: Die Borversorgung von Raps im Hinblick auf Ertragsleistung und Anfälligkeit gegenüber Pilzkrankheiten: Ergebnisse aus Gefäß- und Felderhebungsuntersuchungen in Schleswig-Holstein. Dissertation, Kiel

Phosphorus Deficiency

Phosphorus is, like nitrogen, a major constituent of important cell components such as proteins.

Symptoms

The leaves of phosphorus deficient plants are dull purple and later shiny red to orange in colour ❶, ❷. The first symptoms are visible on the older leaves but, if the deficiency persists, the growth of the whole plant is reduced, the stems are thin and the older leaves die prematurely.

Sulphur Deficiency

Sulphur is an essential element for oilseed rape and serves to construct cell components such as proteins and mustard oils.

Although rape needs much sulphur like all species of crucifers, deficiencies are rarely seen except in areas where aerial deposition from industrial processes has been curtailed in recent years.

Symptoms

The symptoms of sulphur deficiency resemble closely those caused by nitrogen deficiency ❶, ❷. The margins of leaves become pale green and then yellow to red in colour ❸, ❹, ❼. The veins are cleared, and with persisting deficiency, the whole plant is stunted, the lateral extension of the leaf lamina is reduced producing narrow, brittle and erect leaves ❺, ❻. More or less pronounced malformations occur on leaves during growth. In contrast with nitrogen deficiency, sulphur deficiency appears firstly on the younger

leaves. During flowering, sulphur deficiency becomes evident by pale to white discolouration of the petals. Pods affected by severe sulphur deficiency are reddish ❼ and thickened ❽. Seed yield is reduced.

Literature

Schnug, E., 1986: Schwefelversorgung im intensiven Rapsanbau, Raps **4**, 86–89.
Schnug, E., De La Sauce, L. und Pissarek, H. P., 1984: Untersuchungen zur Schwefelversorgung von Raps, Landwirtsch. Forsch. SH. 41, 662-673.

Glossary

Abiotic: Not living

Acervulus: A subepidermal, saucer-shaped asexual fruiting body producing short conidiophores and conidia

Antheridium: Male reproductive structure of some lower fungi (Oomycetes)

Apothecium: An open cup-shaped fruiting body of some Ascomycetes

Appressorium: The swollen tip of a hypha that facilitates adhering and penetration into the host by a fungus

Ascocarp: The fruiting body of ascomycetes bearing or containing asci

Ascospores: A sexually produced spore borne in an ascus

Ascus: A saclike structure containing ascospores (usually eight)

Caterpillar: Type of larva with additional legs on the abdomen

Chlamydospore: A thick-walled, asexual spore formed by the modification of a cell of a hypha

Chlorosis: Yellowing or blanching of normally green tissue

Cleistothecium: An entirely closed ascocarp

Cocoon: Protective cover of the pupa of certain insects

Conidiophore: A specialized hypha on which one or more conidia are produced

Conidium/Conidiospore: Asexual organ of fungal multiplication

Cyst: The dead carcase of female nematodes containing eggs

Diapause: Resting period

Disease cycle: The chain of events involved in disease development

Ectoparasite: A parasite feeding on a host from the exterior

Endoparasite: A parasite which enters a host and feeds from within

Epidemic: A widespread and severe outbreak of a disease

Epidermis: The superficial layer of cells on plants

Fructification time: The time between initial infection by a fungal pathogen and the production of spores

Fruiting body: A complex fungal structure containing spores

Gall: A swelling produced on a plant as a result of infection by certain pathogens or infestation by insect pests

Gamete: A sexual reproductive cell

Gametangium: A cell or organ in wich gametes are formed

Haustorium: A projection of hyphae into host cells which acts as a penetration and absorbing organ

Hypertrophy: A plant overgrowth due to abnormal cell enlargement

Hypha: A single branch of a mycelium

Hypocotyl: Lower stem part of plants between roots and cotyledons

Incubation time or latent period: The period of time between penetration of a host by a pathogen and the first appearance of symptoms

Infection: The establishment of a parasite within a host plant

Infection time: The period of time between the first contact with the host and the establishment of the parasite within the host

Instar: Stage in the development of an insect

Intercellular: Between cells **Intracellular:** Within cells

Larva: In the development of insects the stage which follows the egg stage

Lesion: A localised area of diseased tissue

Maggot: Head- and legless larva

Microorganism: Very small living entities, visible only by microscope

Microsclerotium: Very small sclerotium

Mixed infection: Simultaneous infection by different pathogens

Mosaic: Symptom characterised by intermingled patches of normal and light green or yellowish tissues

Mycelium: Complex of fungal hyphae

Necrosis: Death and discolouration of tissues

Obligate parasite: A parasite that in nature can grow and multiply only on living organisms

Oogonium: Female reproductive structures of some lower fungi (Oomycetes)

Oospores: A sexual spore produced by the union of two morphologically different gametangia (oogonium and antheridium)

Organism: Living entity

Parasite: An organism living on or in another living organism (host) and obtaining its food from the latter

Pathogen: An entity that can cause disease

Pathogenesis: The development of a disease

Plasmodium: Multinucleate aggregate without cell walls (Myxomycetes)

Polyphagous: Eating many different kinds of food

Prognosis: Forecast on disease development and damage

Pseudothecium: Fruiting body containing ascospores produced by certain Ascomycetes

Pupa: Penultimate stage in the development of certain insects, preceding the adult stage

Pycnidium: An asexual, spherical fruiting body lined inside with conidiophores and producing pycnospores

Pycnospore: A spore produced in a pycnidium

Resting spore: A thick-walled spore of a fungus which is resistant to extremes in temperature and moisture

Sclerotium: A compact mass of hyphae capable of surviving under unfavourable environmental conditions

Seedborne: Transmitted by or living in seeds

Soilborne: Transmitted by or living in soil

Spermatia: Unicellular male sexual cells similar to spores

Spermagonium: Fruiting bodies of shape similar to pycnidia but containing spermatia

Spore: The reproductive unit of fungi consisting of one or more cells; it is analogous to the seed of green plants

Sporangium: A structure in which spores are produced

Sporulation: Production of spores

Stroma (ta): Compact mycelial structure on or within which fructifications are usually formed

Susceptibility: The inability of a plant to resist a pathogen

Symptom: The external alterations on a plant as a result of disease or of pest attack

Threshold: The incidence/serverity of disease, numbers of pests or extent of damage which merits treatment for control

Threshold, economic: The level of damage above which the benefits of treatment are greater than its cost

Tumour: A malignant overgrowth of tissues

Vector: An animal able to transmit a pathogen

Virosis: Disease caused by a virus

Virus: A submicroscopic obligate parasite

Zoosporangium: A sporangium which contains or produces zoospores

Zoospore: A spore bearing flagella and capable of moving in water

Zygote: A diploid cell resulting from the union of two gametes

General References

Special References

AID, 1986: Integrierter Pflanzenschutz, Nr. 32, Bonn.

Anon., 1966: Atlas der Krankheiten und Schädlinge der Ölpflanzen. Landwirtschaftlicher Staatsverlag, Prag, in Zusammenarbeit mit VEB Deutscher Landwirtschaftsverlag, Berlin.

Anon., 1978: Colza d'hiver. Cahiers technique n° 3, Maladies, CETIOM, Paris, 16 pp.

Anon., 1985: Cahiers techniques du Colza d'hiver insectes et d'autres ravageurs. CETIOM, Paris, 55 pp.

Bergmann, W., 1983: Ernährungsstörungen bei Kulturpflanzen – Entstehung und Diagnose – VEB Gustav Fischer Verlag, Jena, 614 pp.

Bergmann, W., 1983: Farbatlas Ernährungsstörungen bei Kulturpflanzen für den Gebrauch im Feldbestand, VEB Gustav Fischer Verlag, Jena, 254 pp.

Boerema, G.H. and Verhoeven, A. A., 1980: Check-list for scientific names of common parasitic fungi. Series 2d: Fungi on field crops: vegetables and cruciferous crops. Neth. J. Pl. Path. 86, 199-228.

Buhl, C. und Schütte, F., 1971: Prognose wichtiger Pflanzenschädlinge in der Landwirtschaft, Paul Parey, Berlin und Hambur, 364 pp.

Davies, J.M.L., 1986: Diseases of oilseed rape. In: Scarisbrick, D.H.. and Daniels, R. W. Oilseed Rape. Collins, London, 195-236.

Decker, H., 1969: Phytonematologie. VEB Deutscher Landwirtschaftsverag, Berlin, 526 pp.

Godan, D., 199: Die Schadschnecken. Eugen Ulmer, Stuttgart, 467 pp.

Hoffmann, G. M. und Schmutterer, H., 1983: Parasitäre Krankheiten und Schädlinge an landwirtschaftlichen Kulturpflanzen. Verlag Eugen Ulmer, Stuttgart, 323-374.

Hossfeld, R.; 1987: Schadensschwellen bei tierischen Rapsschädlingen. Raps, 5. Jg. (2), 70-72.

Kirchner, H.-A., 1974: Krankheiten und Schädlinge von Raps, Rübsen und Senf. In: Klinkowski, M., Mühle, E., Reinmuth, E. und Bochow, H., Phytopathologie und Pflanzenschutz. Bd. 11, Akademie Verlag Berlin, 440-446.

Kirchner, H.-A., 1975: Grundriß der Phytopathologie und des Pflanzenschutzes. VEB Gustav Fischer Verlag, Jena, 159-174.

König, K., 1984: Krankheiten und Schädlinge beim Raps. In: Heitefuß, R., König, K., Obst, A. und Reschke, M. Pflanzenkrankheiten und Schädlinge im Ackerbau. DLG-Verlag, Frankfurt/M., 76-91.

Krüger, W., 1984: Raps, Krankheiten und Schädlinge. Semundo Saatzucht GmbH, Hamburg, 120 pp.

Paul, V. H., 1988: Praktische Methode für den einheitlichen Gelbschalenfang von Schadinsekten in Raps. Raps, 6. Jg. (1) 54.

Peres, A., 1985: Colza d'hiver: symptomes et identification des maladies au laboratoire. CETIOM, Paris, 96 pp.

Putnam, L. G. and Burgess, L., 1979: Insect Pests and Diseases of Rape and Mustard, Publication No. 48. Rapeseed Association of Canada. Winnipeg, 32 pp.

Regnault, Y., Laville, J. et Penaud, A., 1987: Cahiers technique Colza. Maladies CETIOM, Paris, 40 pp.

Roder, W., Feyerabend, G. und Rogoll, H., 1975: Landwirtschafter Pflanzenschutz, VEB Deutscher Landwirtschaftsverlag, Berlin, 329-351.

Schütte, F., 1983: Ölfrüchte. In: Heinze, K. Leitfaden der Schädlingsbekämpfung Bad. III, Schädlinge und Krankheiten im Ackerbau. Wissenschaftliche Verlagsgesellschaft mbH, Stuttgart, 683-736.

Schütte, F., Steinberger, J. und Meier, U., 1982: Entwicklungsstadien des Raps. Merkblatt Nr. 27/7 der BBA. ACO Druck, Braunschweig.

Sorauer, P., 1969: Handbuch der Pilzkrankheiten Bd. I, 2. Teil. Die Nichtparasitären Krankheiten. Paul Parey, Berlin, 478 pp.

South, A., 1965: Biology and ecology of Agriolimax reticulatum (Müll.) and other slugs: spatial distribution. -J. Anim. Ecol. 34, 103-177.

Winfield, A. L., 1986: Field pests of oilseed rape. In: Scarisbrick, D. H. and Daniels, R. W. Oilseed Rape. Collins, London, 237-281.

Amelung, D. and Daebeler, F., 1991: Occurrence of fertile apothecia and the epidemiology of Pyrenopeziza brassicae Sulton & Rawlinson (anamorph: Cylindrosporium concentricum Grev.) in the German Democratic Republic. IOBC/WPRS Buletin XIV (6), 147-150.

Brun, H. and Jacques, M. A., 1991: Premature ripening in oilseed rape in France: first report on associated fungi. IOBC/WPRS Bulletin XIV (6), 120-127.

Conn, K. L. and Tewari, J. P., 1990: Survey of Alternaria blackspot and Sclerotinia stem rot in central Alberta in 1989. Can. Plant Dis. Surv. 70, 66-67.

Daebeler, F., Amelung, D. und Zeise, K., 1988: Verticillium-Welke an Winterraps – Auftreten und Bedeutung. Nachrichtenbl. Pflanzenschutzd. DDR, 42 (4), 71-73.

Gladders, P., 1988: Sclerotinia Development in England. IOBC/WPRS Bulletin XIII (4), 83-89.

Günzelmann, A., Paul, V. H. and Kettrup, A., 1991: Occurence, symptomatology, significance and early diagnosis of oilseed rape wilt caused by Verticillium dahliae Kleb. in the Federal Republik of Germany. Proc. 8th Int. Rapeseed Congr., Saskatoon, Vol. 1, 262-264.

Kayser, A. and Heitefuss, R., 1991: Influence of weeds on the infection of winter oilseed rape (Brassica napus L. var. oleifera Metzger) with fungal pathogens. IOBC/WPRS Bulletin XIV (6), 151-154a.

McCartney, H. A. and Lacey, M. E., 1991: Spread of Light Leaf Spot (Pyrenopeziza brassicae) in Oilseed Rape Crops in the United Kingdom. Proc. 8th Int. Rapeseed Congr., Saskatoon, Vol. 2m 454-459.

Morrall, R., A. A., Turkington, T. K., Kaminski, D. A. and Thomson, J. R., 1991: Forecasting Sclerotinia Stem Rot of Spring Rapeseed by Petal Testing. Proc. 8th Int. Rapeseed Congr., Saskatoon, Vol. 2, 483-488.

Saharan, G. S. and Kadian, A. K., 1984: Epidemiology of Alternaria blight of rapeseed and mustard. Cruciferae Newsletter 9, 84-86.

Penaud, H., 1987: La maladie des taches blanches du colza. Phytoma, 23-26.

Petrie, G. A. and Vanterpool, T. C., 1978: Pseudocercosporella capsellae, the cause of white leaf spot and grey stem of Cruciferae in Western Canada. Canadian Plant Disease Survey 58 (4), 69-71.

Zornbach, W., 1990: Untersuchungen zur Pathogenese, Epidemiologie und Bekämpfung von Mycosphaerella brassicicola (DUBY) LINDAU, dem Erreger der Ringfleckenkrankheit an Cruciferen. Mitt. Biol. Bundesanst. Land-u. Forstwirtsch., Berlin-Dahlem, Heft 262, 105 pp.

Zornbach, W., 1991: Spread of ring spot (Mycosphaerella brassicicola (DUBY) LINDAU) between oilseed rape and other Brassica crops in Schleswig-Holstein (Germany). IOBC/WPRS Bulletin XIV (6), 141-145.

Index

A

Acute deficiency 118
Albugo candida 59
Alternaria spp. 38, 41, 55,
56, 62
Alternaria brassicae 38–41,
113
Alternaria brassicicola 38, 39
Alternaria alternata 38
Alternaria raphani 38
Aphanogmus abdominalis 93
Apis mellifera 103
Arvicola terrestris 102
Asteromella brassicae 60–61
Athalia rosae 94–95

B

Beet Cyst Nematode 99
Beet western yellows 17
Beneficial Insects 103
Black Water Rat 102
Blossom Beetle 87–89, 117
Blotch Miner 90
Boron Deficiency 121–122
Botrytis cinerea 33, 42–43,
112, 120
Botrytis Stem Rot 33, 42–43
Botryotinia fuckeliana 42
Brassica Cyst Nematode 99
Brassica Pod Midge 92–93,
105, 113, 120

Brevicoryne brassicae 16, 17,
96–98
Bud Wilting 117

C

Cabbage Aphid 16, 96–98
Cabbage Flea Beetle 70
Cabbage gall 72–73
Cabbage Leaf Miner 91
Cabbage Root Fly 90
Cabbage Seed Weevil 84–86
Cabbage Stem
Flea Beetle 16, 68–71, 81,
90, 108
Cabbage Stem Weevil 78–80
Calcium Deficiency 112
Carduelis cannabina 101
Carduelis chloris 101
Cauliflower Mosaic Virus 16
Ceutorhynchus assimilis
18–19, 84–86, 92
Ceutorhynchus napi 74–77,
80, 110
Ceutorhynchus
picitarsis 81–83
Ceutorhynchus
pallidactylus 78–81
Ceutorhynchus
pleurostigma 18, 72–73
Ceutorhynchus
quadridens 78, 80
Ceutorhynchus spp. 90

Clubroot 18–21
Columba palumbus 100
Common Vole 102
Complex of factors 118
Copper Deficiency 120
Cylindrosporium
concentricum 50–54,
55, 59, 60

D

Dark Leaf and Pod Spot
38–41, 112
Dasineura brassicae 86,
92–93, 112
Delia brassicae 90, 112
Delia radicum 90
Deroceras agreste 66
Deroceras reticulatum 66–67
Ditylenchus dipsaci 99
Downy Mildew 22–25

E

Erysiphe cruciferarum 26

F

Finches 101

Frost Damage 31, 108–109
Fusarium 62

G

Grey Field Slug 66–67
Grey Mould Stem Rot 33,
42–43
Growth Splits 117

H

Hail Injury 112–113
Hare 102
Herbicide Damage 114–115
Heterodera cruciferae 99
Heterodera schachtii 99
Honey Bee 103
Hylemyia 90

L

Late Frost Damage 110–111
Leptosphaeria
maculans 27, 29
Lepus europaeus 102
Light Leaf Spot 50–54, 60

M

Magnesium Deficiency 119
Manganese Deficiency 121
Meligethes aeneus 87–89, 116
Microtus arvalis 102
Molybdenum Deficiency 121
Mycosphaerella brassicicola 60–61
Mycosphaerella capsellae 56
Myzus persicae 16, 17

N

Natural enemies 67, 70, 73, 77, 80, 83, 86, 88, 90, 91, 93, 95, 98, 103
Nematodes 99
Nitrogen Deficiency 118
Nitrogen Scorch 117

O

Oryctolagus cuniculatus 102

P

Passer spp. 101

Passer domesticus 101
Passer montanus 101
Peronospora parasitica 22–25, 59
Pest Detection and Targeted Control 104–105
Phoma lingam 27–32, 46, 48, 49, 51, 55, 60, 62, 70, 78, 112, 120
Phorbia 90
Phosphorus Deficiency 124
Phyllotretra spp. 70
Phytomyza rufipes 91
Plasmodiophora brassicae 18–21, 72
Platygaster oebalus 93
Pollen Beetle 87–89, 105, 117
Potassium Deficiency 118
Powdery Mildew 26
Pratylenchus neglectus 99
Pratylenchus penetrans 99
Pseudocerosporella capsellae 55–58, 60
Psylliodes chrysocephala 68–71, 90, 91, 109
Pyrenopeziza brassicae 50–54
Pythium 62

R

Ramularia armoraciae 59
Ramularia Leaf Spot 59

Rape Stem Weevil 74–77, 79, 80, 105, 110
Rape Winter Stem Weevil 81–83
Reticulated Field Slug 66–67
Rhizoctonia solani 62–63
Ring Spot 60–61
Root Lesion Nematode 99

S

Scaptomyza flava 90
Sclerotinia sclerotiorum 33–36, 42, 44, 48
Sclerotinia Stem Rot 33–36, 42, 44, 47
Sore Shin & Damping off 62–63
Sparrows 101
Spray threshold 67, 70, 73, 77, 80, 83, 86, 88, 90, 91, 93, 95, 98
Stem Canker 27–31, 46, 60
Stem Eelworm 99
Stem Rot 33–36
Sulphur Deficiency 125–127

T

Thanatephorus cucumeris 62
Trichomalus perfectus 86

Turnip Gall Weevil 72–73
Turnip Mosaic 16
Turnip Sawfly 94–95
Turnip Yellow Mosaic 16
Typhula gyrans 44–45
Typhula Root Rot 44–45

V

Verticillium dahliae 46–49, 55, 56, 70, 78, 99
Verticillium Wilt 46–49
Verticillium Stem Rot 46

W

White Leaf Spot 55–58, 60
White Rust 59
Wild Rabbit 102
Wilt 46–49
Woodpigeon 100

Y

Yellow Dish Trap 104

Acknowledgement of Photographs

M. von Abercron, Bundesrepublik Deutschland
122 (1), 123 (4)

BASF, Limburgerhof, Bundesrepublik Deutschland
37 (16), 118 (1), 120 (1), 123 (5), 124 (2)

R. Büchi, FAP, Zürich, Schweiz
73 (3), 78 (3), 79 (7), 81 (1), 84 (1, 2), 92 (3), 95 (2), 96 (1)

H. Brun, INRA - Le Rheu/Pathologie végétale, Rennes, Frankreich
56 (4), 58 (7)

S. Carre - INRA/Zoologie, Lusignan, Frankreich
86 (4)

R. Casper, BBA, Braunschweig, Bundesrepublik Deutschland
17 (1)

CETIOM, Paris, Frankreich
55 (1), 56 (5), 58 (9), 81 (2), 82 (4)

N. Cramer, Rendsburg, Bundesrepublik Deutschland
126 (7)

F. Daebeler, Rostock, Bundesrepublik Deutschland
62 (1)

E. Dorn, Bundesrepublik Deutschland
45 (5, 6)

P. Gladders ADAS, Bristol, Großbritannien
55 (3), 58 (3), 60 (1)

K. Graichen, Aschersleben, Bundesrepublik Deutschland
17 (2)

A. Günzelmann, Soest, Bundesrepublik Deutschland
49 (10)

Kali und Salz AG, Kassel, Bundesrepublik Deutschland
118 (2), 119 (2), 122 (2), 124 (1)

K. König, München, Bundesrepublik Deutschland
68 (1), 72 (2), 73 (4), 74 (1, 2), 75 (4), 78 (1, 2), 83 (3), 87 (1), 88 (2), 92 (1, 2), 95 (4)

Kölnische Hagelversicherung, Köln, Bundesrepublik Deutschland
112 (1, 2), 113 (3, 4)

W. Krüger, Braunschweig, Bundesrepublik Deutschland
90 (2)

V. H. Paul, Soest, Bundesrepublik Deutschland
18 (1, 2, 3), 19 (4, 5, 6), 22 (1, 2, 3, 4), 24 (5, 6, 7), 25 (8, 9, 10), 26 (1, 2, 3, 4), 27 (1, 2, 3), 28 (4, 5, 6), 29 (7, 8, 9, 10), 32 (11, 12, 13, 14), 33 (1), 34 (2, 3, 4, 5, 6, 7), 36 (8, 9, 10, 11, 12, 13), 37 (14, 15), 38 (1, 2, 3, 4), 39 (5, 6, 7), 41 (8, 9, 10, 11), 42 (1, 2, 3, 4, 5, 6), 43 (7, 8, 9, 10, 11), 44 (1, 2, 3), 45 (1), 46 (1, 2), 48 (3, 4, 5, 6, 7), 49 (9, 11, 12, 13, 14), 50 (1, 2, 3, 4), 51 (5, 6, 7), 53 (9, 10, 11, 12, 13), 54 (14, 15, 16, 18, 19), 58 (10), 62 (2), 63 (3, 4, 5), 66 (1, 2), 67 (3, 4), 68 (2), 70 (3, 4), 71 (5, 6), 74 (3), 75 (5, 6), 77 (7, 8, 9 10), 79 (4, 5), 80 (6), 86 (5), 88 (3, 4), 91 (1, 2), 93 (4, 5), 96 (1, 2), 97 (3, 4), 98 (5, 6, 7), 100 (1, 2, 3), 101 (1, 2), 103 (1, 2), 104 (1, 2), 108 (1), 109 (2, 3, 4), 110 (1, 2), 111 (3, 4), 114 (1, 2), 115 (3, 4, 5), 116 (1, 2), 117 (1), 118 (1)

Ch. Rawlinson, London, Großbritannien
53 (8), 54 (9), 55 (2, 4)

Schering AG, Düsseldorf, Bundesrepublik Deutschland
72 (1)

K. Schlüter, Rendsburg, Bundesrepublik Deutschland
94 (1), 95 (3)

A. Schmitt, BBA, Darmstadt, Bundesrepublik Deutschland
90 (1)

E. Schnug, Kiel, Bundesrepublik Deutschland
120 (1), 121 (1, 1), 122 (3), 125 (1, 2, 3), 126 (4, 5, 6), 127 (8, 9, 10)

U. Steck, München, Bundesrepublik Deutschland
37 (17)

W. Zornbach, Braunschweig, Bundesrepublik Deutschland
60 (1, 2), 61 (3, 4, 5)